ATOMS FOR THE WORLD

ATOMS FOR THE WORLD

UNITED STATES PARTICIPATION

IN THE CONFERENCE ON

THE PEACEFUL USES OF ATOMIC ENERGY

By *LAURA FERMI*

14406   THE UNIVERSITY OF CHICAGO PRESS

Library of Congress Catalog Number: 57-6977

THE UNIVERSITY OF CHICAGO PRESS, CHICAGO 37
The University of Toronto Press, Toronto 5, Canada

© *1957 by The University of Chicago. Published 1957*
Third Impression 1961. Composed and printed by THE
UNIVERSITY OF CHICAGO PRESS, *Chicago, Illinois, U.S.A.*

FOREWORD

The historic address by President Eisenhower on December 8, 1953, evoked an extraordinarily unanimous and enthusiastic response from an alarmed and frustrated world.

Six years had elapsed since the Soviets had rejected the Baruch proposals, and the dread prospect of an eventual, catastrophic, atomic war hung suspended over mankind. The people of the world felt themselves trapped in an impasse out of which there seemed to be no avenue of escape.

But from the President's speech sprang the Atoms for Peace program, and a hopeful world has now, after three years of negotiation, succeeded in crystallizing a charter which is to bring into existence the Agency the President had envisioned. During the three years, the applications of atomic energy for human welfare have continued to advance. In this advance, the greatest stride is generally conceded to have been the International Conference on the Peaceful Uses of Atomic Energy which was held at Geneva in the summer of 1955.

The conference provided the first opportunity in many years for exchange of technical information and ideas among the world's scientists and engineers; it re-established and widened the lines of scientific communication which in happier prewar years had been open to science for universal welfare.

Mrs. Laura Fermi, widow of Enrico Fermi, attended the conference as historian for the United States delegation. *Atoms for the World* is her story of the part taken by the United States. It is an intimate and informative account, illuminating the hopes and plans of the participants, the problems encountered, the people involved, and the successful culmination of the months of planning and work entailed by our participation in the conference. It is hoped that from this book readers will gain a clearer understanding of the achievements of the conference and the contribution of the United

States to its success. Those who will have the responsibility for conducting such conferences in future years may also benefit from the experiences of the participants in this enterprise.

Lewis L. Strauss

*Chairman, U.S. Atomic Energy Commission
and Chairman of U.S. Delegation to the
International Conference on Peaceful Uses
of Atomic Energy*

PREFACE

This is not *the* history of the first Conference on the Peaceful Uses of Atomic Energy, or the more limited history of the United States participation in the conference. It is only *a* story of that participation as seen by a layman with no special technical or humanistic training. It lacks historical objectivity and balance, scientific understanding and thoroughness. Perhaps worse, it does not attempt to give credit where credit is due—to enumerate all individuals and organizations that contributed to the success of the conference, to describe and weigh those contributions, or to evaluate the importance of individual roles.

To the best of my knowledge all the events here related took place, all the persons here portrayed are real. But the selection of episodes has been left more to chance and to my own inclination than to an evaluation of intrinsic worth. Talkative delegates may have found their way into these pages in larger numbers than taciturn ones; some facts may have been dealt with at greater length than others for no better reason than that they made a more amusing story. Nevertheless, I have followed some guiding principles: I have tried to show the magnitude of the effort, the extent of the cooperation and of the good will that made this conference possible and successful; to give some idea, even if spotty and superficial, of the topics presented in it; and to re-create the amazing atmosphere in which it evolved. From the enormously vast material that would make an exhaustive history of this conference I have chosen what I thought might be of greater interest to the general public. Here I may have made a gross error of judgment and considered the public's interest much too similar to my own.

The reader who seeks more than this book can offer will find ampler, more technical, and much more satisfactory information in the Technical Reports of the Atomic Energy Commission, and in the proceedings of the conference published in English, French, Russian, and Spanish under the sponsorship of the United Nations.

LAURA FERMI

CONTENTS

LIST OF ILLUSTRATIONS

1 *AFTERTHOUGHTS*

From August 8 to August 20, 1955, the delegates of seventy-three countries and of seven specialized agencies of the United Nations assembled in the Palais des Nations in Geneva, in the largest conclave ever convened under the aegis of the United Nations, to discuss the peaceful applications of atomic energy. It was a historic event unique in conception and results. In the past there had been different types of conferences: political, educational, scientific, economic, and many others, each fostering one well-defined path of human advance. But never before had a technical conference of governments been summoned at which high government officials sat together with technical and scientific experts; never before had a gathering from which politics had been so deliberately and successfully banned proved to be of such great political import; never before had a scientific meeting exceeded the boundaries of one discipline to explore so many others. This new atomic energy enters all fields of knowledge: physics, chemistry, metallurgy, and engineering make it possible; biology, medicine, agriculture, and industry take advantage of its applications; economy is affected by the prospect of its large-scale production; law is to regulate it.

Nuclear science was developed during the war, in great secrecy, and was first applied to war purposes. Then, and in the postwar years, only a few countries participated in its development; not many nations had the financial power, the initiative, or the ability needed for extensive and costly programs of research and large staffs of specially trained personnel. After the war, secrecy was lifted in part, but much information was withheld, both on the military and the peaceful uses of atomic energy, because the two cannot be separated entirely—in the furthering of peaceful applications, materials may be produced that could be used in weapons. Yet progress belongs to all, and secrecy cannot for long restrict it within limited boundaries. So the countries that knew how to produce atomic energy agreed to disclose as much information as their security laws

1

permitted, to exchange data, and to offer their knowledge to those who did not have it.

The force that moved fourteen hundred delegates, as many ob- servers, and nine hundred men reporting to the public through the information mediums and made them assemble in Geneva from all corners of the world might well have been fear—fear of the de- structiveness of the atom. But fear alone could have produced no concrete achievements had it not combined in many minds with faith in the atom as a helpful servant of mankind. So the delegates assembling in Geneva during the days that preceded the conference brought along a hopefulness and an optimism that were cautious and wary at first. These feelings mounted steadily after the opening of the conference, freed themselves of previous reservations, turned into elation and euphoria. The Palais des Nations, the legacy of the old League of Nations and a symbol of men's continuing endeavors to attain world unity, became the seat of a working utopia.

It was as if all that did not pertain directly to the conference, even one's own previous feelings and opinions, were forgotten, or deliberately discarded from the mind; as if the many differences, the non-settled issues still dividing mankind, were of no importance; as if the only fact that mattered in the world were to prove one's good will and to show it in action for two weeks in Geneva. In the Palais des Nations there was no East or West; there were no "cur- tains," no totalitarian states, no democracies—only men eager to learn or to disclose what they had learned. A wealth of technical and scientific information was made available to all. And all, whether from the underdeveloped or from the best industrialized countries, forgetful of the many difficulties still to be surmounted, of the strenuous years of research that lay ahead before atomic power could be plentiful, dreamt together of deserts turned green and marshes reclaimed, of new industries, of diseases overcome, of crops made more abundant.

These men may have been overidealistic, detached from reality, but through their sincere, perhaps naïve, enthusiasm the conference achieved a success that surpassed all hopes. Here was at last a ground on which people from both sides of the Iron Curtain could meet in friendship and in a mutual trust that had a chance to spread slowly to wider fields; science was brought back to the truly international level on which it belongs; channels of communications that had been closed for long years were re-established; scientists who had not even known of each other tasted the pleasure of getting acquainted and finding common fields of interest. The world came to realize the sincerity of the United States desire to put the atom to peaceful uses and to share the resulting benefits with other countries. The extensive, objective coverage of the conference by newspapers, radio, and television did much to overcome the widespread ignorance, to dispel the confusion in the minds of the public about atomic energy and what it can accomplish, and to overcome the belief that nuclear energy is a synonym for destruction.

Some of the spirit of good will and co-operativeness may have antedated the Conference on the Peaceful Uses of Atomic Energy, a spirit left in the air at Geneva by another international gathering of great moment, the conference of the Big Four chiefs of government. President Eisenhower had met for six days, from July 18 to July 23, with Prime Minister Anthony Eden of England, Premier Edgar Faure of France, and Premier Nikolai A. Bulganin of the Soviet Union, in the same Palais des Nations at Geneva where the scientists met later. President Eisenhower had advocated for some time a change of spirit, a reciprocal confidence that would make co-existence possible; and this change of spirit had appeared to take place at Geneva. There were no concrete achievements, no treaties signed, no agreements written. The question of German reunification was set aside for the foreign ministers to consider in October; the four disarmament proposals advanced by the four chiefs of state were placed in the hands of the United Nations; President Eisenhower proposed a system of inspection based on exchange of blueprints of military establishments and on reciprocal permission for aerial reconnaissance and aerial photography; this plan was hailed and neither rejected nor accepted. Yet in the conversations among the Big Four the unprecedented friendliness and sincerity convinced the world that both the United States and the Soviet Union were then striving for peace and trying to avoid war.

This "spirit of Geneva" lasted for the two weeks that elapsed between the closing of the "Summit" meeting and the opening of the Conference on the Peaceful Uses of Atomic Energy and contributed to the success of the latter. Because the two conferences were so close in time; because they both dealt with aspects of the atomic age—the first with the ways to avoid atomic warfare, the second with the means to make atomic energy benefit humanity; because President Eisenhower's Atoms for Peace program, of which the second conference was an implement, was considered at the first; because the "spirit of Geneva" pervaded both—posterity may tend to consider them as one, or to attribute a relation of cause and effect to them, a relation which did not in fact exist. The second conference was the first conceived, the longer planned, the one for which greater efforts were made toward organization, and possibly the one with longer-lasting effects: the winds of politics may blow this way or that; the results of a political meeting may be upset. At the second, the scientific conference, an irreversible step was taken: the advances of science and technology that were disclosed are now the property of mankind and can never be confined again behind national barriers.

2 EVOLUTION OF AN IDEA

The sequence of the events that led to the Conference on the Peaceful Uses of Atomic Energy began December 8, 1953. By four o'clock in the afternoon of that day a large crowd had gathered behind barricades outside the headquarters of the United Nations in New York. Inside, thirty-five hundred people from sixty countries had taken their seats in the Assembly Hall; throughout the United States, radio and television sets were on: President Eisenhower was going to address the General Assembly of the United Nations.

It was not known what he had to say; but the fact that he was returning from Bermuda, where he had met for four days with Prime Minister Winston Churchill of Great Britain and Premier Joseph Laniel of France, gave this occasion historical significance. So the men and women behind the barricades next to the building of the United Nations welcomed their President with loud cheers as he turned to them, his face tanned by the southern sun. Inside the hall the audience rose to their feet and acclaimed him with a prolonged ovation. Then he started to speak, earnestly, humbly; and the world learned of things that had been on his mind and heart "for a great many months."

In the new "language of atomic warfare" President Eisenhower recalled the first atomic explosion during World War II and described the immensely larger force of modern weapons. He stressed the "hideous damage," the "probability of civilization destroyed—the annihilation of this irreplaceable heritage of mankind," in the event of an atomic war.

This, the longer part of the speech, is not the best remembered, for the second part raised new hopes that this tremendously destructive force could be made to serve mankind. ". . . Peaceful power from atomic energy is no dream of the future," the President said. "That capability, already proved, is here—now—today. Who can doubt, if the entire body of the world's scientists and engineers had adequate amounts of fissionable material with which to test and develop their ideas, that this capability would rapidly be transformed into universal, efficient, and economic usage?

"To hasten the day when fear of the atom will begin to disappear . . . I . . . make the following proposals:

"The Governments principally involved, to the extent permitted by elementary prudence, to begin now and to continue to make joint contributions from their stockpiles of normal uranium and fissionable materials to an International Atomic Energy Agency. We would expect that such an agency would be set up under the aegis of the United Nations. . . .

"The more important responsibility of this Atomic Energy Agency would be to devise methods whereby the fissionable material would be allocated to serve the peaceful pursuits of mankind. Experts would be mobilized to apply energy to the needs of agriculture, medicine . . . to provide abundant electrical energy in power-starved areas of the world. . . .

"The United States would be more than willing—it would be proud to take up with others . . . the development of plans whereby such peaceful use of atomic energy would be expedited . . . the Soviet Union must, of course, be one. . . ."

The President concluded with a promise: ". . . the United States pledges before you—and therefore before the world—its determination to help solve the fearful atomic dilemma—to devote its entire heart and mind to find the way by which the miraculous inventiveness of man shall not be dedicated to his death, but consecrated to his life."

Enthusiasm exploded in the audience, which had been listening in perfect stillness. Everyone sprang again to his feet, applauded and kept on applauding, unanimously; even the delegates from countries behind the Iron Curtain jumped up at once and joined in the applause.

Thus the Peaceful Atom was formally introduced to the world. Little had the layman heard about him before, because during the postwar years he had remained in hiding behind the security laws made necessary by his more assertive brother, the Destructive Atom.

Despite the welcome without precedent that the President's address received, his plan encountered difficulties at once. The Soviet

Union took the position that a complete ban on the use of atomic and hydrogen weapons should be considered at the same time as, and during the course of, any discussions on the peaceful uses of atomic energy. This attitude defeated the spirit of President Eisenhower's Atoms for Peace proposal, which meant, in substance: "Since we cannot reach an agreement in questions affecting the security of our countries, let us co-operate in a field that will endanger no one and may bring benefits to all."

This is the background against which the Conference on the Peaceful Uses of Atomic Energy was conceived weeks later, early in 1954. It is a characteristic feature of this conference that the interest in it was to be weak at first and to gather momentum slowly as the months went by and 1954 turned into 1955, as the few people who had faith in its usefulness talked to other people and engaged their help.

The story of the conference begins with two main actors: the one a tall, straight man from Virginia, who during the Second World War served as a rear admiral; the other a short, round-shouldered scholar with thick eyebrows branching suddenly upward. The first a public figure whose round face and glasses had often appeared in the daily press; the second a Nobel Prize winner, well known only in intellectual circles: Admiral Lewis L. Strauss, Chairman of the Atomic Energy Commission, and Professor Isidor I. Rabi of Columbia University, the chairman of the General Advisory Committee to the Atomic Energy Commission.

Admiral Strauss took the Atoms for Peace plan very much to heart. A fervent idealist easily aroused by imaginative causes, he had always taken many persons and many things to heart during the course of his life: his wife and son, and later his grandchildren (he liked to call himself a "professional grandfather" after the birth of the third); his Jewish religion; and science, to which he had directed his interest and his admiration and which he regretted not having studied more formally. After finishing high school as valedictorian of his class, Lewis Strauss had chosen to go to work rather than to college. He worked first in his father's business in Virginia, then as a volunteer under Herbert Hoover when the latter was director of European relief after the First World War, and later as a banker. His enormous drive, favored by an exceptional physical endurance, pushed him forward and made it possible for him to engage in other activities on the side, prominent among which was the absorbing of large amounts of knowledge from avidly read books and from conversations with his friends. The atomic field, from its inception, was especially appealing to him. Before the Second World War, physicist friends came to discuss their researches and their difficulties with him—and he helped to ease their financial burdens until the United States government took over.

In supporting atomic science Lewis Strauss could not compete with the government, but he could go along with it. In 1946 he accepted President Truman's invitation to serve on the new Atomic Energy Commission. He had just left the Navy Reserve, where in four long years he had risen from the rank of lieutenant commander to that of rear admiral. The civilian Atomic Energy Commission was created in 1946 to take over the Army's wartime Manhattan Project, and Admiral Strauss was the first Commissioner to be appointed by Truman. He served until 1950, when he retired and went back to private finance. But when, upon taking office, President Eisenhower looked around for an atomic adviser, the choice again was Strauss.

The President and his adviser were similar in many ways: they were both men of deep faith, both devoted to the Republican party, both dedicated to duty. And they shared the same avocation: they raised Angus cattle, the President on his farm at Gettysburg, Mr. Strauss at Brandy, near Culpepper in Virginia, on peaceful hilly grounds, part of which had belonged to his grandfather Leopold, an immigrant from Germany. Strauss was proud of his six hundred head of cattle. When the President bought a Brandy Rock year-old bull calf, Strauss and his manager, after much consultation, decided to dress up the animal for delivery to Gettysburg with a "real fancy halter."

President Eisenhower asked his atomic adviser to find a chairman for the Atomic Energy Commission. But when Admiral Strauss made his suggestions, the President appointed him to the post. The chairman of the Atomic Energy Commission would naturally be eager for the success of the Atoms for Peace plan, but Strauss's interest was already aroused. He had been one of the party that accompanied President Eisenhower to the Bermuda conference. While meetings were being held at the top level, Strauss and his friend Lord Cherwell, Churchill's atomic adviser, had discussed President Eisenhower's ideas for his address to the General Assembly; they had also talked about possible ways of implementing the Atoms for Peace proposal that the President was to make. Strauss suggested an international conference. With the world in the shape it then was in, Lord Cherwell had been dubious about the suggestion. Strauss, extremely sensitive to his friends' opinions, had stored the idea away in one of the innumerable pigeonholes of his mind. In his enthusiasm for the Atoms for Peace plan, while the President was giving the finishing touches to it on the flight back to New York from Bermuda, Strauss had helped the team of staff writers, typists, and secretaries to prepare copies of the speech.

Despite the difficulties later encountered by the President's proposal, Chairman Strauss did not want it shelved indefinitely. At a meeting with the General Advisory Committee, early in 1954, he asked for suggestions to further the plan; and Professor Rabi, whom nobody had ever accused of lacking imagination, proposed the calling of an international conference to discuss the peaceful applications of atomic energy. Strauss's idea jumped out of the pigeonhole in his mind. So the scientists thought along the same lines he did! The idea *must* be good! Admiral Strauss undoubtedly responded to Rabi's proposal with his well-known grin, once described as slightly owlish.

Strauss and Rabi exchanged views on the ways the conference could be organized. They thought the United States would sponsor it. They thought some two or three hundred scientists from both the East and the West could be invited. Rabi, like all scientists accustomed to being hampered by lack of funds, was concerned about the financial aspects of the project: who would foot the bill? Strauss, an optimist through whose hands much money had passed, was confident that he could raise the 300,000 dollars that might be needed. With his usual promptness and lack of hesitancy, he launched into the project. Boldness of attack was essential.

In a letter dated April 14, 1954, addressed to James Hagerty, the White House Press Secretary, Admiral Strauss sought authorization to announce the conference, despite the lack of formal plans for it.

To avoid the delay of routine channels, he did not write directly to the President. He wished to make the announcement in a speech he was to give five days later—the prepared speech, he said once with modest humor, was dull and uninteresting; he needed something to enliven it. In the letter to Hagerty he said:

"Some days ago I mentioned to the President that in furtherance of his plan he might ask the National Science Foundation or the National Academy of Sciences to consider calling a conference of scientists of all countries for some later date in the year specifically to talk about peaceful uses of atomic energy in line with his proposal. The President thought well of it. Suggested that I talk with [Secretary of State John] Foster Dulles which I did . . . who also thought well of it. . . ."

On April 19, in the scheduled address before the Los Angeles World Affairs Council, Chairman Strauss said:

". . . I am privileged to state that it is the President's intention to arrange through a national scientific organization to convene an international conference of scientists at a later date this year. This conference, which it is hoped will be largely attended and will include the outstanding men in their professions from all over the world, will be devoted to the exploration of the benign and peaceful uses of atomic energy. . . ."

Meanwhile actual plans proceeded slowly. Only Strauss and Rabi, who had become chairman of a committee for the conference, seemed to have faith in the success of an international gathering. They could kindle little interest in others. Even the directors of the National Laboratories, meeting in the spring at Tapoca Lodge near Gatlinburg in the Smokies, gave lukewarm reception to the idea. Later these men worked around the clock to prepare the United States contribution to the conference, the success of which was due in large part to them. But at first they could not be aroused. Perhaps the beauty of the surrounding hills with their luxuriant vegetation and the mildness of the weather were not conducive to intellectual effort. When the feasibility of the conference was discussed at Tapoca Lodge, the difficulties inherent in the secrecy of a great part of atomic knowledge seemed formidable: the Atomic Energy Act of 1954 had not yet been passed by Congress, and no one knew how much information it would be possible to disclose. A conference on the international level did not seem to be worth the effort.

There was further discussion later at a luncheon around Chairman Strauss's desk at which were present, among others, the presidents of the National Academy of Sciences and of the National Science Foundation, and Mr. John Hall, liaison officer between the Atomic Energy Commission and the State Department. Eating off trays, everyone thought aloud, with no prepared plans, about possibilities and difficulties. Should the conference be sponsored by governments or scientific academies? Should its scope be limited to the field of power or should it include every aspect of atomic research and its applications in the fields of medicine, biology, chemistry, and industry? Would it be possible to hold the meeting in the United States, from which the McCarran Act of 1950 would exclude many persons? Should a pleasant island—Bermuda, Nassau, or Jamaica—be considered instead? If such an island were chosen, would the conference receive sufficient press coverage? Should a steering committee of different countries be set up? All difficult questions. The only conclusion drawn that day, if any conclusion was drawn at all, was that nothing more could be done unless scientists of friendly nations were consulted. John Hall went to seek the opinion of the State Department; Rabi wrote memoranda and made more plans.

In August Rabi flew to Europe. This was a turning point in the organization of the conference: from then on prominent scientists abroad were drawn into the planning, ideas were exchanged, programs began to take shape and be defined.

Rabi had known before leaving for Europe that unless he brought along concrete suggestions his trip would be futile. He ought to have, first of all, a tentative topical agenda. Circumstances helped him prepare it: He had arranged to spend the early part of the summer at the Brookhaven National Laboratory on Long Island, one of whose objectives is to provide research facilities for university scientists. The program at Brookhaven covers all phases of fundamental nuclear research, a large part of it centering on a research reactor. Specific topics include fundamental studies of atomic nuclei; production and utilization of radioactive isotopes; the effects of radiations on materials, on plants and animals; and the disposal of radioactive wastes. There is at Brookhaven a research hospital where radiations are used for both medical diagnosis and treatment. A list of all the activities at Brookhaven that Rabi obtained from the leaders of the various groups constituted the first tentative agenda for the future conference.

Rabi landed in London and was driven directly to Cambridge, where a meeting was held over a much prolonged luncheon with several top English scientists and one from Canada. The most important of these men for the purpose of this story is Sir John Cockcroft, the director of the United Kingdom Atomic Energy Establishment at Harwell. Everyone at the luncheon was more polite than enthusiastic at first. When Rabi presented the agenda he had prepared at Brookhaven, the others professed concern about the inclusion of medicine: physicians were known to move in large crowds, and the conference ought to be kept within reasonable boundaries, perhaps three hundred participants. It was thought that the conference should be sponsored by the United Nations. It was not quite clear where it should be held: the English favored Cambridge, where an entire college could be taken over; Rabi suggested Rome; Copenhagen was considered; later The Hague extended an invitation to call the conference there. Opinions diverged also on the matter of the amount of information to be disclosed. The Atomic Energy Act of 1954 had just been passed and the prospects of making public much knowledge so far kept secret had greatly improved. On the other hand, the law would have to be carefully studied and interpreted, and policies established to safeguard national security.

At the end of this meeting Sir John Cockcroft took Professor Rabi along to his summer house at Cley next the Sea, on that stretch of the eastern coast of England which runs from east to west and faces north. Rabi and Cockcroft had much in common: a physically similar build, short and slight; both in their upper fifties; both nuclear scientists and Nobel Prize winners: Rabi for work on the magnetism of nuclei; Cockcroft for having built the first accelerating machine of charged particles, together with Dr. Walton, back in 1932, and for having caused the first splitting of lithium nuclei into two alpha particles, using protons accelerated in this machine. Cockcroft and Rabi also shared a deep interest in international and especially European questions. It was Rabi who had suggested, at a meeting of UNESCO in Florence in 1950, that the European countries pool their financial and scientific resources to build one center of nuclear research equipped with accelerators, which the single nations could not afford. After this suggestion was accepted by several European countries, and while the European Center for Nuclear Research (CERN) was in its preliminary stages, Sir John Cockcroft had been the most sympathetic to the enterprise, the least insular of the British, who for some years had been uncertain and unresponsive toward the project, which in the end they joined.

At Cley next the Sea, it was too cold to swim or to go fishing, Rabi recalled later. Walking along the beach, the two friends discussed possible items of an agenda for the conference. They called on Professor Edgar D. Adrian at his nearby summer house and received his advice on the biological part of the agenda. Sir John Cockcroft, now a devoted supporter of the conference, promised Professor Rabi that he would put the essence of their conversations on paper and send it to him in the United States.

Leaving Cley next the Sea, Rabi stopped briefly in London to report to the United States diplomatic service on the progress of his activities respecting the future conference and for an interview with Sir Edwin Plowden, Chairman of the United Kingdom Atomic Energy Authority. He left England well pleased and, after a brief stay in France, flew back to the States. He was to go to Europe three more times during the next twelve months: later in 1954 for a meeting of the European Center for Nuclear Research and for more talks with Sir John; in May, 1955, for the second meeting of the Advisory Committee for the Geneva conference, and the following August for the conference itself. "Strange how I was destined to travel," he remarked later, with the prolonged low giggling that always revealed his presence, even in a crowd where he was lost among taller men. An inveterate New Yorker, he had seldom left the city in his early years; the first time he could remember crossing the Hudson River was to go to college at Cornell University in Ithaca, New York.

Following his first trip to Europe, Rabi spent two weeks at the Oak Ridge National Laboratory in his capacity of consultant to the Atomic Energy Commission. There was at the laboratory a twenty-nine-year-old physicist, tall and strong, with great self-reliance and many good ideas that he seldom kept to himself but expressed easily and fluently. About a year later this young man, Robert A. Charpie, was to become Assistant Director of Research at the Oak Ridge National Laboratory. Rabi, who had occasion to see him repeatedly, was impressed by his energy and drive. There was no mention of the conference during those two weeks, but when Rabi received a topical agenda from Cockcroft with the official approval of the British government's Interdepartmental Committee, he passed it on to Charpie asking him to study it and amplify it if needed. At the same time Rabi suggested that Bob Charpie try to pool suggestions from the Oak Ridge scientists for an inclusive technical program for the conference and in particular for the United States participation in it.

The topical agenda, as Bob Charpie received it, was essentially the one that Rabi had prepared at Brookhaven with the help of its leaders and that in England had been enlarged by British and Canadian scientists, mostly at Cockcroft's suggestion. In Oak Ridge it was further enlarged and became very similar to that later adopted by the General Assembly of the United Nations: the agenda, as planned, extended over twelve full working days. The first three were to be devoted to topics of general interest meant for scientists in all fields; the meetings consequently would be held in general sessions. Some of the subjects selected for the general sessions were such that the nations in which little or no nuclear research was being carried out could still contribute papers, for example on the various countries' requirements of energy during the next fifty years and on their deposits of uranium and thorium. After the first three days the topics were to become more specialized. To allow for thorough presentation without excessively prolonging the conference, Charpie thought of running three concurrent sets of sessions: one would cover reactors and reactor physics; a second would deal with chemistry, metallurgy, and technology; a third would include biology, medicine, and radioactive isotopes.

From Oak Ridge, and from Robert Charpie in particular, came other suggestions for the United States participation that will be related in the next chapter. It is time at this point for a brief report on progress elsewhere.

Professor Rabi's consultations with scientists in this country and abroad were followed up in various ways: there were meetings with diplomats and other representatives of England and Canada; State

Department representatives sat in on all these meetings and advanced the diplomatic and political points of view; Sir John Cockcroft visited the United States; and Chairman Strauss filled various important roles. He said once that all he did for the conference was to sign an "awful" number of documents. He did not specify how many of these gave sanction to much needed immediate financial support or to essential speed-ups in administrative procedures. At each new project that the scientists proposed for our participation, Strauss, an admirer of inventiveness but tensely aware of the approaching deadline, would say: "Go ahead, do what you want, provided you'll have it finished a full month before the opening of the conference."

Indeed, the Strauss household was far from relaxed during the period of preparations for the conference. Mrs. Strauss complained that even when she and her husband sought a weekend of seclusion at Brandy Rock, the farm which they both loved, there was hardly a half-hour without a telephone call from Washington. Once, on a Sunday morning, Strauss, feeling acutely the need for rest, went fishing with a neighbor down a nearby river, out of sight and earshot of the farm. He came back late for dinner, physically exhausted, grimy, very different from the impeccably dressed Chairman of the Atomic Energy Commission. The car had got stuck; the river was muddy. "And the fish?" asked a lady guest. The Chairman blushed: they had had a long string of fish hanging on the outside of the car, he said. It was not there when they got to his neighbor's home. It must have fallen off on the road. He claimed his clothes were smelly (fish, of course) and rushed indoors to change. For the entire morning Strauss had forgotten the international conference— and nobody worried about the loss of the fish.

Besides signing papers and facilitating matters for the scientists as much as he could, Lewis Strauss performed another function that, though less noticeable to others, may have been of greater consequence. He kept President Eisenhower up to date on the progress of preparations and received the President's frequent advice. If Professor Rabi was occasionally given to discouragement because of his temperament, if Chairman Strauss became apprehensive at times despite his apparent confidence, the President, by contrast, never displayed any doubt about the ultimate success of the conference and of his Atoms for Peace program.

At the President's direction, Secretary of State John Foster Dulles, speaking before the General Assembly of the United Nations on September 23, 1954, proposed an agenda item for that body. It called for the creation of an international atomic energy agency including nations from all regions of the world; and for the convening of an international scientific conference as early as possible in 1955, under the auspices of the United Nations. In his address Secretary Dulles also revealed that the United States and the Soviet Union were willing to publish all documents exchanged in the course of private negotiations following President Eisenhower's proposal of December 8, 1953. It is from these documents that the position of the Soviet Union, previously mentioned as a difficulty for the furthering of the proposal, emerged: that a total ban on atomic weapons should precede the creation of any organ for the co-operation in the development of peaceful uses of atomic energy. The United States left the door open for more negotiations, "but," said Secretary Dulles, "we shall no longer suspend our efforts to establish an international atomic energy agency"; consequently he introduced the agenda item.

Other factors may have influenced later Soviet decisions. In that same address Secretary Dulles announced the opening by the Atomic Energy Commission of a reactor training school for foreign students and the invitation to physicians and surgeons from abroad to participate in the work of our cancer hospitals in which atomic energy techniques are among the most hopeful approaches to controlling this menace to mankind. Six more countries—Australia, Belgium, Canada, France, the Union of South Africa, and the United Kingdom—joined the United States in the sponsoring of a resolution in accordance with Dulles' proposal; a few weeks later the United States took another concrete step, when its government allocated 100 kilograms (220 pounds) of atomic fuel to be used in research reactors throughout the world. (In June, 1955, Chairman Strauss announced the allocation of another 100 kilograms of fuel.) A draft resolution was submitted to the United Nations General Assembly in plenary session on December 4, 1954, and was adopted by unanimous vote. To that extent at least, the Soviet attitude had changed.

In its final form the resolution consisted of two parts, the first of which indorsed the proposed establishment of an international atomic energy agency. The second decided that an international technical conference of governments should be held under the auspices of the United Nations; invited to it all state members of the United Nations or of the specialized agencies; suggested that the conference should be held no later than August, 1955; and established an Advisory Committee of representatives of Brazil, Canada, France, India, the Union of Soviet Socialist Republics, the United Kingdom, and the United States of America.

August, 1955, if not too close, was not far away. (Here was the deadline against which Chairman Strauss was working.) There was no time to waste. It was necessary that the Advisory Committee meet in January and no later, and that the seven countries forming it name their representatives at once. It appeared logical that the United States and England should name Dr. Rabi and Sir John Cockcroft, respectively (John V. Dunworth had represented the United Kingdom at a preliminary series of meetings). The other members of the committee were Dr. J. Costa Ribeiro, alternate to Minister Jayme de Barros of Brazil, Dr. W. B. Lewis of Canada, Dr. Bertrand Goldschmidt of France, Dr. Homi J. Bhabha of India, and Academician D. V. Skobeltzin of the U.S.S.R.

About this time Dr. Rabi made a decision that in his mind was "very important." He wrote a letter to Admiral Strauss to say that the task of organizing the United States participation in the conference was no part-time job for a professor at Columbia University who had to teach and advise his students. He would not mind sitting on the Advisory Committee, but he resigned "from everything else" connected with the conference and suggested that a man be sought who could devote his full time to the United States technical participation in it.

As late as the last days of 1954, Homi Bhabha, a dark-haired, thickset Indian theoretical physicist in his middle forties, knew nothing of an international scientific conference. This is not surprising in view of the fact that most of the preparations were so far unofficially under way in the United States and in England. Sir John Cockcroft, it is true, had spread the news about the conference among European members of the few-months-old European Atomic Energy Society, of which he had been elected president for the first year. France had been consulted. Canada had participated in the informal talks from the beginning, but the rest of the world as yet knew nothing.

A few days before Christmas Bhabha flew from his home in Bombay to Bangalore, a city in the center of the southern tip of India, for a vacation and to do some work at leisure. He was leaving many cares behind, for in an unusually rapid and brilliant career he had become Secretary of the Indian Department for Atomic Energy and Chairman of the Indian Atomic Energy Commission; moreover, he was director of the Tata Institute of Fundamental Research in Bombay. This institute was named after the Tata family to which Bhabha's mother belonged, one of the most prominent Parsi families in India, owner of steel mills among the largest in the world.

No sooner had Bhabha set foot on the ground at the Bangalore airport than he was taken to a telephone for a long-distance call from the Foreign Minister in Delhi. Then only did he learn of the United Nations resolution, of the forthcoming conference, and of the fact that Prime Minister Nehru had expressed the opinion that he, Bhabha, ought to be the Indian representative on the Advisory Committee. Bhabha's personality was particularly suited to a role of this kind; with the grand manner of the wealthy Easterner he combined the aristocratic ways of an international diplomat, acquired during his many travels in Europe and elsewhere in the years since he finished school. He accepted this new task, shortened his vacation, and arrived in New York in the middle of January.

The Advisory Committee, composed of the seven representatives and their staffs, held its first meeting with Secretary-General of the United Nations Dag Hammarskjöld from January 17 to 28, 1955, in New York. John Hall and Robert Charpie were on the United States staff accompanying Rabi. When the committee convened on the morning of January 17, two items were up for discussion, the topical agenda and the rules of procedure. The latter were considered first, and this was perhaps a mistake: the meeting seemed to fall into the almost traditional pattern of delay because of lengthy procedural arguments raised by the Soviet Union. The Soviet member of the Advisory Committee was Academician D. V. Skobeltzin, a tall, ponderous, white-haired man who talked, according to his inter-

preters, in the old-fashioned Russian peculiar to ex-government officials. He was possibly following a natural bureaucratic inclination,
or his tendency to protraction and debate may have reflected a non-
avowed state of mind of all the members: apprehension that their
endeavors would prove futile, that failure was more likely than success, and uncertainty of what, in any case, might be the achievements of the conference that they were trying to organize.

To break the impasse, Dr. Bhabha proposed to postpone discussion of the rules of procedure and to examine the topical agenda
first: the agenda represented the essence of the conference and it
was common sense to give it priority over procedure, which was
only the machinery that was to move the meetings. The members of
the Advisory Committee took the afternoon off for private consultations and reconvened the next morning. As soon as they found themselves on scientific rather than on diplomatic grounds, they worked
rapidly and in good agreement.

The agenda prepared by Professor Rabi, Sir John Cockcroft, and
Dr. Robert Charpie in collaboration with other scientists from England, Canada, and the United States was not the only one on the
floor. Another agenda had been prepared by Dr. Gunnar Randers,
a Norwegian physicist who was Mr. Hammarskjöld's scientific adviser and member of an internal working party for the conference
in the United Nations. Dr. Randers' agenda placed more stress on
the production of atomic power and less on its applications, for he
felt that the field of power production was the only one in which
new information could be disclosed and that the inclusion of other
topics would unduly burden the program. The other agenda was
accepted. After this, the rules of procedure were passed without
much difficulty.

The Advisory Committee decided also the place and dates of the
conference and advised Mr. Hammarskjöld on the nomination of a
president. Although in their earlier discussions Rabi and Cockcroft
had considered other cities more favorably than Geneva, once the
United Nations assumed the sponsorship of the conference everyone
agreed that Geneva was the best place. One factor, perhaps the
major one, was the United Nations requirement that the papers
presented orally must be transmitted at the same time in the four

official languages—English, French, Russian, and Spanish. Geneva was the only European city provided with ample facilities for simultaneous translation into several languages; to set up the necessary wiring and equipment in any other place would mean a considerable expense, which none of the participating countries was prepared to undertake. The selection of Geneva, of course, limited the choice of dates; the many international meetings held in the Palais des Nations, the European office of the United Nations, are usually scheduled long ahead of time. The period from August 8 to August 20 was the best available and was reserved for the conference.

The members of the Advisory Committee were divided at first on who should fill the role of president of the conference. Many names were suggested and there was considerable debate. In the end all members agreed on Homi Bhabha, who had been suggested by the French representative, and on their recommendation Secretary-General Hammarskjöld duly appointed Bhabha president of the future conference. Professor Whitman, head of the Chemical Engineering Department at the Massachusetts Institute of Technology and a member of the General Advisory Committee to the Atomic Energy Commission, was named conference secretary-general. Later, physicist Viktor S. Vavilov of the Institute of Physics of the Soviet Union Academy of Sciences was made deputy secretary-general, to help Professor Whitman.

On February 1 the Secretary-General of the United Nations, in accordance with the resolution adopted by the General Assembly on December 4, sent out letters of invitation to the eighty-four nations that were members either of the United Nations or of its specialized agencies, and to these agencies. Attached to each letter were the accepted preliminary topical agenda and the rules of procedure. One of these rules, which was quoted in the invitations, provided that each participating state "may be represented at the Conference by no more than five representatives. . . . The representatives may be accompanied by such number of advisers as may be required, in the general interest of the Conference, to ensure adequate presentation and discussion of technical papers." A third annex accompanying the invitations may have caused some surprise: it was an announcement that the Soviet Union would submit a paper titled "The First

U.S.S.R. Atomic Plant for Industrial Purposes and Methods of Developing Atomic Power." During the course of discussions on the peaceful uses of atomic energy in the Political Committee of the United Nations, preceding the introduction of the resolution for the international agency and the technical conference, the Soviet Union had disclosed that on June 27, 1954, the first industrial plant in the world to produce electric power from atomic energy had started operating in the U.S.S.R.

3 THE OIC

The letter from the Secretary-General of the United Nations inviting the United States to participate in the Geneva conference went to the State Department. Two weeks later, on February 14, the Department, while retaining the over-all political responsibility, asked the Atomic Energy Commission to take primary responsibility for the technical planning of the United States participation in the conference.

Explorations and activities undertaken so far on the assumption that there would be a conference now became official and needed to be co-ordinated. In line with the suggestion advanced by Professor Rabi when he resigned from "everything" connected with the conference except his post on the Advisory Committee, the Commission sought a man capable of directing the technical participation and able to devote his full time to this task. The choice fell on Dr. George Weil, a physicist in his middle forties and a long-time reactor expert.

In December, 1942, in Chicago, when the first chain reaction was produced in the first reactor ever made—called a "pile" at that time—Dr. Weil had manually operated the cadmium rod that controlled the reaction and had thus "ushered in the atomic age." After helping to build reactors at Hanford during the war, he had become Assistant Director of the Reactor Development Division of the Atomic Energy Commission, and, when he left this post to become a private consultant in atomic matters, he had been retained as consultant to the Commission. When the call came to direct the technical program for the conference, he set aside temporarily all other matters and went back to work in the Commission building on Constitution Avenue.

Weil assumed his post in the latter part of February. His new official title was "Technical Director of the Office for the United States Participation in the International Conference on the Peaceful Uses of Atomic Energy." The name of the office appeared in all its magnificent length on the official stationery. But the same stationery, as if out of pity for the persons who were to answer, bore the advice to reply to: "Office for International Conference," and in the Commission the office became known simply as the OIC.

Dr. Weil soon realized that, if his title was ponderous, his task was no less so. For a few weeks, while he tried to become oriented, to get the United States program going and to co-ordinate it with that of the United Nations, the pages of his calendar were solid with appointments, seven days a week. He talked to an incredible number of people, seeking information and advice, looking for collaborators and contributors to the conference. Each evening, when he finally reached his home in Cabin John, Maryland, after a drive unduly lengthened by traffic, he was too exhausted even to play with his three-year-old son Stephen, the most important member of his household.

George Weil had, of course, to become acquainted with the plans so far made for the conference. The technical program had been in part outlined and some preparations were under way. During the preceding fall, at Professor Rabi's request, Dr. Charpie had gathered ideas from scientists at the Oak Ridge National Laboratory and had undoubtedly contributed his own. These ideas were evaluated and sifted at a meeting in Washington with members of the Commission staff before the United Nations sent out invitations to the various countries.

The conclusion reached at this meeting was that the United States program, besides the presentation of technical and scientific papers covering all sections of the topical agenda, should include an operating reactor if feasible, technical exhibits, a technical library, films, and a set of books containing selected reference material on atomic energy. The reasoning behind this decision was that the United States should present its development in the peaceful applications of atomic energy as thoroughly as possible and prove the sincerity of its offer to share its knowledge with other nations. A temporary committee was set up to plan for the exhibits, the members of which were Dr. Robert Charpie, already introduced to the reader; Dr. Alberto F. Thompson, Director of Technical Information of the Atomic Energy Commission; Dr. George G. Manov, assistant to the Assistant General Manager for Research and Industrial Development; and Mr. Don Cowen of the Oak Ridge National Laboratory.

All these activities, going on before the conference was officially called, were co-ordinated at the commission top level by Dr. Willard F. Libby. He had assumed this role soon after his appointment as Commissioner in early October. Although the press characterized him as "rather solemn," he could put his solemnity aside and brighten up on such occasions as the victory of his favorite team at the World Series. Commissioner Libby, a nuclear scientist himself and the inventor of a method for dating anything that at one time contained living material by measuring its content of radioactive carbon, saw at once that an international technical conference could do a great deal to advance science. He gave his personal support to early activities and encouraged preliminary steps before official sanction could be given them, if their delay appeared to endanger the success of our program. After the conference was called, through the period of preparations, unofficial short cuts became almost the rule in matters relating to the conference; and the long administrative paths were abandoned, an indispensable policy in view of the tight time schedule.

Dr. Libby gave his blessing to the technical program as outlined by Robert Charpie and the temporary committee. Charpie set to work and began by writing some 250 letters to United States industries and organizations inviting them to participate in the technical exhibits. Then he was recruited by Professor Whitman for his staff of "scientific secretaries," of whom more will be said later. His abilities were thus placed at the service of the United Nations to organize and co-ordinate the contributions of the individual countries. So far as the United States preparations are concerned he fell out of the picture.

This is where matters stood when George Weil took office. As soon as he could find time between interviews, Weil sat bent over his imposing desk, his oval face made longer by a forehead that showed an untimely propensity to spread backward, and pursued Charpie's job of letter-writing. He dictated and signed some three thousand letters to individuals and organizations, informing those to whom Charpie had already written that now an office for the United States participation in the international conference had been set up, requesting others to send technical papers or to suggest possible contributions they might make.

Meanwhile he put together his staff, which he recruited from the best-suited men working at the Atomic Energy Commission. He went at his work with a calm thoroughness and a deceptive lack of excitement. But those who knew him well could see in the flickers of his small black eyes that the deadline of the conference was his constant concern, that worry about it sharpened his glances, as if he were trying to pierce the future and see the conference as it would unfold the following August. There was no time for lengthy comments or for protracted discussions. In his quiet way, George Weil whipped out decisions that others chose to follow as orders.

His office was on the second floor of the Atomic Energy Commission building, in a room conveniently located near that of Commissioner Libby, with whom he shared an entrance hall and whom he kept informed on the progress of preparations for the conference. Other members of the OIC staff were not so lucky and were scattered here and there over the three floors of the building, wherever a bit of space was available. Thus on many doors, seemingly at random, there appeared the sign "Office for International Conference."

At a far end of the long corridor on the first floor was the office of Mr. Thomas O. Jones, Administrative Officer of the OIC. In Tom Jones, Weil found his right hand. A cheerful person who delighted in simple things like the discovery of a really efficient ball-point pen, Tom Jones took charge of innumerable matters. He looked as if he never had anything pressing to attend to, but managed to provide secretaries and offices, typewriters and printed stationery, contracts for personnel, travel orders and travel vouchers, with the ease of a magician pulling rabbits out of a hat.

Jones did not want a cumbersome administration and a huge administrative office; so he went around to various Atomic Energy Commission offices and in each of them found a man to take particular responsibility for matters concerning the OIC. Perhaps, for instance, he walked into the mail room and with a cheerful smile approached the man he thought would suit his needs. Perhaps he pulled his new ball-point pen out of his pocket and said: "To write on all kinds of paper the ball-point must be very fine." Then he could have told the man that the OIC wished to have its mail, tons of it, handled separately, not with all that of the AEC; would he please see to it? Tom Jones visited in succession the security office, the personnel office, the finance office, the legal office, and the supply and construction office, which supplied everything from desks to credit cards for cables. In each office he secured someone's help. Thus George Weil could enjoy the luxury of forgetting these matters.

Dr. Paul McDaniel, Deputy Director of the Commission's Division of Research, had his office on the third floor of the building. He assumed the responsibility for organizing and co-ordinating the presentation of the technical papers. The task was huge. By May 1 his office had received eleven hundred abstracts, of up to five hundred words each, submitted by scientists and engineers from colleges and universities, from national laboratories, from hospitals, research institutions, and industrial groups—an overwhelming response that greatly surpassed the most optimistic expectations. Eleven hundred authors all over the country were waiting for a word from Dr. McDaniel before starting to write their papers in full.

Paul McDaniel set up seven review committees and several subcommittees of scientists in the various fields of nuclear science who, under his direction, evaluated the abstracts, eliminated the trivial or non-pertinent and the duplications, checked them for restricted data, and arranged some in groups to be worked into survey papers. When they finished examining abstracts, the papers started to come in and had to be reviewed in the same manner. The review committees kept at their tedious work steadily. From March to July, Paul McDaniel, in shirt sleeves, with a half-absorbed, half-resigned expression, burrowed through tall stacks of papers. He raised his eyes only now and then to dictate a letter to an author or to consult with one of his younger assistants. "There is nothing glamorous in sorting papers," said Dr. McDaniel later, "no human angle story." He had not noticed that his suit hung more and more loosely on him as time went by. But the outcome of his labor and that of his committees was rewarding. The United States contribution of papers was excellent and very strong: 550 papers were submitted to the United Nations, and all were to be published in the proceedings of the conference, in the four official languages. Of the 550 papers, Paul McDaniel and his staff recommended 175 for oral presentation at Geneva.

Presentation of papers to scientific meetings is usually not this thoroughly organized. Scientists are individualists and they like to decide by themselves whether to participate or not in a conference and what to present to it. But this was not simply a scientific conference; it was also a "technical conference of governments." The various countries' governments and not their scientists were responsible for the presentation of their atomic programs. In the United States this responsibility had been assumed by the Atomic Energy Commission, and it was only natural that the Commission should strive for the best and most coherent presentation of its program, that it should ask the co-operation of its most competent man in each field and make certain that there was no duplication of effort. The organization of the Commission was well suited for this purpose: the directors of the Atomic Energy Commission's National Laboratories met regularly and could be consulted on policies and means to obtain the maximum results from the total effort for the conference. They could report to and consult with the leaders of their laboratories, who in their turn could ask men in their groups to prepare abstracts and papers, according to what they were best suited for. Abstracts and papers came also from universities and many other organizations, not only from the National Laboratories. Paul McDaniel and his review committees integrated them all into a coherent whole.

Another reason for reviewing the United States papers before sending them to the United Nations was to check that the declassification rules had been properly interpreted. The word "declassification" may not be found in a dictionary but is widely used wherever security is involved. To declassify means to permit disclosure of information which was previously "classified," namely, either secret or confidential. The large amount of previously classified information presented at Geneva was not declassified especially for the conference but as a result of one of the normal periodic changes in the rules governing the release of information, as defined in the classification guide.

The Atomic Energy Act of 1946, under which the Commission was established, was written shortly after the end of the Second World War, at a time when atomic power for civilian use was still a distant goal. President Eisenhower realized that to make this goal a reality the participation of private industry was necessary, and he recommended to Congress that the 1946 Act be revised accordingly. The new Atomic Energy Act of 1954, passed by Congress on August 30 of that year, while still placing the greater stress on defense and security, added emphasis on the development of peacetime uses of atomic energy; for this it granted authority to the Commission to widen international co-operation, to increase private industrial participation, and to encourage dissemination of information. The new act specifically instructed the Commission to "maintain a continuous review" of restricted data and of classification guides "in order to determine which information may be declassified . . . without undue risk to the common defense and security."

In October, 1954, shortly after the passage of the Atomic Energy Act of 1954, the United States, England, and Canada held another of their periodic declassification conferences, this one at Harwell, the United Kingdom Atomic Energy Research Establishment. Similar meetings had taken place from time to time since the end of the war, this being the seventh. As the result of this meeting the existing classification guide was revised in accordance with the new law. No consideration was given to special declassification for the Geneva conference because the conference was still a somewhat vague idea in the minds of only a few men, most of them in the United States. But at Harwell, Sir John Cockcroft repeatedly asked his American colleague, Dr. Warren C. Johnson, whether plans for the conference were progressing. Dr. Johnson was attending the meeting as chairman of the Committee of Senior Reviewers, which "advises the Commission on classification and declassification matters." He was also a member of the General Advisory Committee to the Atomic Energy Commission. Even he had heard nothing definite about the conference.

The revised guide required the approval of the three governments and was not published until the following April. In the United States, declassification problems did not end here. Interest in the success of the conference had by then greatly mounted, and it was hoped that much information could be disclosed at Geneva. Both the Atomic Energy Commission and the scientists desired as liberal an interpretation of the guide as possible, consistent with national security, and the Committee of Senior Reviewers met often with the Division of Classification to study the guide and decide the extent to which these wishes could be met.

In the light of these facts it is easy to understand the magnitude of the task of the Division of Classification under the direction of Dr. Charles D. Luke and his deputy, Mr. Charles L. Marshall. It was their responsibility to ascertain that the authors of papers had not exceeded the safe boundaries set up in the declassification guide, to suggest for this purpose possible revisions of papers, and to keep authors informed of any modification in declassification policies.

The responsibility inside the OIC for exhibiting an operating research reactor at the conference was assigned to Dr. George Manov. The story of the reactor erected in Geneva to demonstrate the feasibility and the uses of small reactors will be the subject of a later chapter. It may be noted here that this, perhaps the most daring project among all contributions to the conference from all countries, required the approval of the United Nations and of the Swiss government. While this approval was pending, plans for this project could not be revealed.

Dr. Alberto Thompson took charge of the technical exhibits, library, and films, and of the set of reference volumes. The technical exhibits were to constitute a tangible illustration of the topics presented orally and to evolve parallel to them, along the lines of the topical agenda, from the production of materials needed in reactors to the applications of radioisotopes. At the exhibits, everyone to whom the specialized language of science was unintelligible, and the experts in one branch of science only, would be able to take in through their eyes the whole panorama of recent progress in atomic science, which they would not so easily comprehend through their ears from the technical papers alone.

At the time when Robert Charpie had sent out letters asking industries to participate in the exhibits, no other country had expressed interest in exhibiting. Therefore the question of space in the very roomy Palais des Nations had not arisen. But when the United Nations learned of the United States intention to exhibit, they decided to inform the other countries of this intention and to ask them whether they too wished to exhibit. Dr. Weil and Dr. Thompson thought it advisable to have someone check on the space available in Geneva. A man with some experience of exhibitions was essential; and, even better, a man who also knew something of the type of exhibits that the OIC was planning. Mr. Richard Brecker filled the requirements: employed by the United States Information Agency, he had worked on the exhibit "Atoms for Peace," which that agency was currently showing in West Germany.

Dick Brecker, an active young man full of initiative, went to Geneva. Professor Whitman, the Secretary-General of the conference, was also there, on a trip of which more will be said later. An examination of the Palais des Nations and talks with Mr. Adrian Pelt, Director of the European Office of the United Nations, revealed that space in the Palais would become limited if several countries wished to exhibit. Only highly technical displays of interest to the scientific delegations and for which the governments of the exhibiting countries would be responsible should be held in the Palais. Mr. Pelt suggested that other displays, of either a commercial or a more popular nature, could be set up in another building in Geneva, the Exhibition Hall.

Dick Brecker made quick decisions. He selected the most suitable hall in the Palais des Nations, Salle XV, and placed an option on it for the United States, pending application for space from other countries. He went to see the Exhibition Hall: it was huge, certainly large enough even for the United States Information Agency's popular "Atoms for Peace" exhibit, including a large, full-scale model of a reactor. Why not move the whole exhibit to Geneva? Acting for the Information Agency, Dick Brecker put an option on space also at the Exhibition Hall.

In the light of the information that Dick Brecker brought back to Washington, the OIC policies about exhibits had to be modified. The OIC could not be responsible for commercial exhibits, or for the popular one planned by the Information Agency at Brecker's suggestion; but the latter could be enlarged to accommodate some of the material which commercial firms had meanwhile proposed to display. Other commercial firms could participate in the Exhibition Hall trade fair, which the United Nations had said they would welcome but would not feel responsible for in any way. Dr. Weil performed the sad task of informing each organization whether any of its material could be included in the government's technical exhibits and, if not, whether the United States Information Agency would consider that material for inclusion in the popular display, or whether the organization was to make its own arrangements for the trade fair. One of the prospective exhibitors in the United States, upon receiving Dr. Weil's letter, from which he learned that he was left on his own, grabbed the telephone and called the Exhibition Hall in Geneva. Decisions and letter-writing had been so fast that nobody at that hall knew anything yet about the trade fair.

Meanwhile, George Weil, realizing that an exhibit set up entirely by scientists might not be the most aesthetic, had engaged the help of a commercial firm, Design and Production, Incorporated. He had many interviews with the firm's president, Mr. Leonard Rennie, a spare, wiry man with great ability and determination. It was decided that, with the advice of scientists of the Atomic Energy Commission and under Mr. Rennie's competent supervision, Design and Production was to build the framework for the exhibition and to assemble the displays of individual exhibitors into a coherent whole.

One afternoon in early May a few men from Design and Production arrived in George Weil's office carrying a huge gray box. There was immediate commotion. Even George Weil became visibly excited: he helped set the box on the table with solicitous care; he called in people from other rooms. The box was the scale model of the technical exhibits, and when its lid, which formed the ceiling, was lifted, one could see the inside arrangements in detail: the partitions, the showcases and shelves, the strong color scheme (each exhibitor had received a fact sheet specifying colors: reactor area, neutral gray No. 195, with full strength red orange No. 34 to be used in limited quantities, for instance), the large reactor models, even the lighting.

Design and Production had built the model to fit the shape of Salle XV, but when George Weil saw the model he had not yet received a final answer from the United Nations confirming the United States request for this room, despite his anxious telephone calls and telegrams across the ocean. Dr. Weil and Dr. Thompson took a calculated risk: they gave their approval to the model and kept their fingers crossed. There was no time to waste.

A while later the United Nations, having received requests for exhibit space in the Palais des Nations from Belgium, Canada, England, France, the Scandinavian countries, and the Soviet Union, made definite allocation of available halls. The United States was assigned Salle XV, as well as a smaller hall in which the technical library could be installed.

The technical library was to be a concrete example, more effective than a printed list of contents, of the libraries comprising unclassified and declassified literature on atomic energy that the Atomic Energy Commission had been making available to foreign nations upon request since late 1954. Upon learning that a room was available, Dr. Weil and Dr. Thompson decided to set it up as a working reference library where delegates of all countries could pursue their studies in the atomic field while they were at the conference.

Difficulties concerning the exhibits did not upset George Weil too much. His first big headache, he recollected later, was caused by the introductory volume to the eight volumes of selected reference material, a set of which was to be presented as a gift to each foreign representative. Of the eight volumes, six were assembled from existing publications, declassified according to the new guide, and two were written for the conference. All together they constituted a comprehensive progress report of research and development in the United States and a practical source of information in the field of peaceful uses of atomic energy. It was George Weil's idea to add to the set an introductory volume in four languages, briefly describing the content of each volume. He chose a man to write this description and made arrangements with a publisher to have it translated into French, Russian, and Spanish. A few days before the deadline set by the publisher for the English manuscript, Dr. Weil found out that the man he had chosen had been unable to fulfil his task because of illness in his family and that another man had been called in. The latter's writing was poor and unacceptable to Weil. Hurriedly he made contact with the original man and a professional writer, who rewrote the introduction over the weekend.

This experience put Dr. Weil on the alert. Things that were started well did not necessarily go on well. Perhaps it would be wise to have the translations of the introductory volume reviewed and see whether they were up to the high standards of the conference. There a confusing situation ensued. The translations had been started late, as a consequence of the delay in the English text. Translators were hired to translate and then others to check the translations. Language specialists double-checked them.

"From then on," said Dr. Thompson with a broad, humorous smile, "no two people ever seemed to agree." Meanwhile all those concerned with the introductory volume were working on tight schedules to meet interlocking deadlines: a delay in completing the translations of the book would cause delay in the printing, stitching, binding, and shipping to Geneva. The introductory volume was almost given up and was completed before the opening of the conference only because the printer gave up a scheduled vacation during the first two weeks of July.

Similar adventures befell translations of the captions for the technical exhibits. Many of the English texts of the captions were prepared by Mr. J. William Young, one of the Atomic Energy Commission's scientists assisting Design and Production with the plans for the exhibits. Others came from the National Laboratories and the National Reactor Testing Station, together with exhibit components. The checking and rechecking of their translations caused a delay in the final printing. The last captions were ready toward the end of July; like the introductory volume, they were rushed to Geneva by plane. There they were glued on the already assembled exhibits.

Most of the translating difficulties derived from the fact that atomic science had created a new terminology, and corresponding foreign terminologies were little known. What did the French call a "scram rod," the safety rod which is inserted in a reactor core in case of emergency, when the order is given that all persons get away? A conscientious scientist wrote to a French colleague to get the correct translation, only to receive an official letter explaining in French that "scram" is an American slang word.

All the work that went into the preparation of the technical films was co-ordinated by Mr. Edwin L. Wilber, under Dr. Thompson's direction. The films to be presented in Geneva were to be technical, not popular, Dr. Thompson decided; but they were not to be too specialized. This was the first decision about the films. The next was to have them in the four official languages. This decision ruled out the possibility of making entirely new films for Geneva: it was realized that there was not much time to translate the scripts and to find narrators in the various languages with satisfactory voices and ways of speaking: a film on safety experiments with a reactor could not be "spoken" by just anyone. Besides, new films would have to be approved by several persons, and sending them from office to office would be a lengthy process. So the seven technical motion pictures for Geneva were chosen or pieced together from existing films or film footage.

When the English scripts were ready, they were given to the Signal Corps for translation. Max G. Kosarin had been in charge of foreign adaptations at the pictorial center of the Signal Corps for fourteen years and knew the problems well. He knew, for instance, that English is the most concise of the four languages and that to say the same things in Russian takes up to 20 per cent more time. Allowances in the scripts must be made accordingly. The Russian language presented other difficulties, as some people spoke it in a formal way, others in a more modern and colloquial manner. Despite these problems and various delays and despite anxieties and misgivings in the OIC, the films in the four languages were ready before the end of July, and the foreign scripts were good.

Of the seven technical films, five dealt with reactors—their development, construction, and uses; these films were produced in the field by the laboratories where the reactors were located. The remaining two films were about radioisotopes and their uses in science and medicine. Besides the seven technical films, two other more popular motion pictures were shown in Geneva, and of those a few words will be said in a later chapter.

Unfortunately for him, Dr. Thompson was to provide a "human angle" side to the story of the OIC, the lack of which Dr. McDaniel had decried. Dr. Thompson became ill the day before he was to leave for Geneva to supervise the mounting of the exhibits. He managed to recover sufficiently to fly to Geneva for the conference, against his doctor's advice, but after nine days he was stricken again and was rushed back home. Thus he missed most of the show he had worked so hard to organize.

George Weil also engaged the help of technical writers to prepare reports and a history of the conference. Because of the shortage of office space, they were shifted around the building and asked to sit in corners of already crowded rooms at desks temporarily vacated by the regular occupants. In the end they were all packed into an office set aside for them, around one large table borrowed from a conference hall.

As time went on, there were changes in the organization of the personnel preparing the Geneva conference; and a new group was set up to deal with newspapers and help disseminate information. Mr. Harry S. Traynor, Assistant General Manager of the Commission, was named executive officer of the United States delegation to the conference. The technical program remained in the hands of the men already mentioned; Mr. Traynor backed them up with detailed attention to the thousands of specific items that had to be followed through on the business side. He pulled all the loose threads together at the right moment and thereby played a most valuable part in assuring that the United States presentations were ready when the conference opened on August 8.

So these were in brief the activities of the OIC in the Atomic Energy Commission. There was of course also the long-established Office of International Conferences in the Department of State, responsible for arranging United States participation in all international conferences. This office financed the travel of the greater part of the United States delegation to Geneva, arranged for passports, found office and hotel accommodations, issued identifications and credentials to the delegates and assisted them in many ways.

Meanwhile at the United Nations the Secretary-General of the conference, Professor Walter Whitman, was very busy. He sensed some hesitancy in the major nations at first, as if each of them were waiting to see what the others would do, how much they would disclose. Countries were slow in informing the secretariat of the number of papers they thought they would present. Under these circumstances it was difficult to evaluate the size of the conference, the staff it would need, and the space requirements for the sessions and exhibits. And the time was short. Professor Whitman thought that direct consultations with the planners of various countries might help. He was to go to Geneva anyhow, to make arrangements for the conference with Mr. Adrian Pelt, Director of the European Office of the United Nations. He combined the two purposes and flew to Europe in March, accompanied by Mr. Brian Urquhart of the United Nations Secretariat.

From Professor Lewis of Canada, Whitman had already received a provisional list of the papers which that country intended to present to the conference. The United States list was rushed to him as he was boarding the plane at Idlewild Airport. Both lists formed the basis of consultations and discussions with Sir John Cockcroft and other scientists in England.

When Whitman left for Paris, he had three lists to show the French. These were examined by Professor Perrin and Dr. Gold-schmidt and "had an invigorating effect upon all present," as Brian Urquhart put it in an informal report on the organization of the conference. The French tackled the problem of their contributions to the conference with renewed enthusiasm and ardor.

Whitman and Urquhart proceeded to Geneva, where they consulted with Mr. Pelt on many organization details, saw the halls that would be available at the Palais des Nations, checked on the facilities for simultaneous translations, and inspected the space available for exhibits.

On their way to Moscow they stopped again in Paris, and over breakfast with Dr. Goldschmidt they received the tentative list of French papers. They were then joined by Dr. Gunnar Randers, the Norwegian scientific adviser to Secretary-General Hammarskjöld, and the three went to Moscow together. In Moscow, Academician Skobeltzin was given copies of the tentative lists of papers prepared in Canada, the United States, the United Kingdom, and France. He seemed to be favorably impressed with them and promised to send a similar list of Soviet papers in a month or so with Viktor Vavilov, who would be arriving in New York then to assume his post as Deputy Secretary-General of the conference.

During his European travels Professor Whitman had another end in mind: he hoped to recruit a group of young scientists from many countries to form a working team of "scientific secretaries" for the conference. He had received the United States assurance that two American scientists, Drs. Robert Charpie and Frederic de Hoffmann, would join this team. From other nations he obtained the promise that they would also send young scientists to New York. Dr. Skobeltzin, in particular, intimated that the Soviet Union might be able to supply two or three men. Professor Whitman's trip was very fruitful. Upon his return he no longer doubted the success of the conference, although by the middle of April only sixteen countries had signified their intention to participate in it.

Dr. Vavilov arrived in New York from Moscow in the middle of

April. The son of a Russian physicist well known in the early thirties who had been president of the U.S.S.R. Academy of Sciences, Viktor Vavilov was an attractive, dark-haired young physicist, with natural good manners and a quiet seriousness that seemed beyond his age. He spoke precise, well-enunciated English, with a little effort, which made his brow wrinkle and his eyes take the shape of triangles. Professor Whitman never failed to give full credit to his efficient deputy. In a memorandum written only four days after Vavilov's arrival Whitman wrote: "Dr. Vavilov . . . has already been most helpful in establishing the closer communication and better understanding which are essential to adequate preparations for the Conference."

The team of scientific secretaries started arriving in New York in early May—nineteen of them from thirteen countries in Europe, Asia, and the Americas. In August, one more was added in Geneva. The young scientist from Pakistan was named Abdus Salam, which means "Servant of Peace," a fact which was considered a good omen. The nineteen of them, or rather the twenty-one, including Professor Whitman and Dr. Vavilov, undertook their work with alacrity. The common goal united them, and they forgot their different origins. They argued often, but on scientific, not political, grounds. They reviewed papers, gave the final form to the conference agenda, and saw that each session had a chairman, a vice-chairman, and two secretaries. Rather regretfully they assigned themselves as secretaries to the sessions: they anticipated with no great pleasure sitting through session after session with little time left for personal scientific contacts with the delegates. They selected the papers to be delivered orally, eliminating duplications, yet trying to balance the contributions of the various countries and to allow small nations to have a part in the program. Because so many factors had to be considered, the papers presented orally at Geneva might not necessarily be the best, they said, but scientific quality would still be the first criterion for selection.

In the latter part of May and during the beginning of June, while the scientific secretaries were busily examining the papers which flowed in at an ever increasing rate, the second meeting of the Advisory Committee took place in Paris, at UNESCO House. The members of the Advisory Committee had taken their own advisers along. The United States party included, besides Dr. Rabi as a member of the committee, Dr. Weil, Robert Charpie, Dr. McDaniel, Mr. John Hall, Mr. Charter Heslep of the Atomic Energy Commission's Public Information Service, and others. Worries and uncertainties about the success of the conference were now dispelled to a large degree, and the committee members found one another quite friendly and congenial.

They discussed the progress of the preparations in their countries and in other nations; assigned to the scientific secretaries the task of selecting papers for oral presentation; considered possible session chairmen and vice-chairmen to be recruited from as many countries as possible; and discussed evening lectures, which had been suggested in the preliminary agenda. This last item had been controversial ever since it was proposed by Professor Rabi and Dr. Charpie as a means of balancing the very specialized sessions with topics of broader interest. Many scientists thought the day schedule of the conference so well packed with learning that evenings ought to offer lighter relaxation than lectures on the principle of complementarity or on the fast particles found in the cosmic radiation. Although support for the evening lectures had increased, there were still dissenters when the meeting opened in Paris. Professor Whitman would have gladly substituted concerts for some of the lectures. It was for the Soviet Union to tip the scales in favor of the lectures: Academician Skobeltzin declared that scientists were to work in Geneva, not to play, and the lectures stayed on the program.

The next step was to select ten outstanding speakers for the ten evening lectures. Each member of the Advisory Committee offered suggestions. Academician Skobeltzin proposed several Soviet scientists, adding after each name, as if to stress their distinction, "He is a member of the Academy of Sciences of the Union of Soviet Socialist Republics." Then it was Professor Rabi's turn. He suggested Professor Ernest O. Lawrence of the University of California, and, with the poker-face that he could assume on some occasions, remarked, "It may be of passing interest that Professor Lawrence also is a member of the Academy of Sciences of the Soviet Union." The remark was followed by a hearty burst of laughter.

The Advisory Committee adjourned its Paris meeting in June and was not to meet again until August in Geneva just before the conference.

Although this history is concerned exclusively with the Geneva conference and mainly with the part that the United States took in it, it would not be complete without the mention of an event that caused much speculation. Around the middle of June our National Academy of Sciences received an invitation from the Soviet Academy of Sciences to a meeting on peaceful uses of atomic energy in Moscow, from July 1 to July 5. It soon became known that invitations had gone to academies of sciences of other countries and to individual foreign members of the Soviet Academy, like Professor Lawrence, so that, in all, scientists from forty-one nations had been invited.

To say that the men who were organizing our participation in the Geneva conference were puzzled by the Soviet move is a great understatement. It is not in the tradition of international meetings to be called two weeks ahead of their opening. The United States system of granting passports is in general faster than that of some European countries. Yet it seems hardly believable that Professor Lawrence, to take one concrete example, could arrange to leave his work in California, obtain a passport or, if he had one already, have it validated for travel in the Soviet Union, secure space on a plane at the height of the tourist season, and turn up in Moscow, all within two weeks. It is not in the tradition of international meetings either, once one is called and long planned, for a nation that has agreed to take part in it and is officially collaborating in its organization to suddenly call another meeting on the same subject without consulting the other participating countries.

Some of the scientific academies, those of the United States and Great Britain among them, declined the invitation on the grounds of the shortness of time and because their member-scientists were busy preparing for the Geneva conference. Some accepted it, and scientists from the close-by Scandinavian countries attended the meeting in Moscow. The greatest attraction was a visit to the Soviet Union atomic power plant, which, as the Russians had previously announced, had been in operation for about a year.

Even before this highly puzzling development, speculations about Soviet science and Soviet contributions to the Geneva conference were quite lively. All references to Russian achievements were qualified by words like "allegedly" or "they claim" or by some other expression of doubt. Such skepticism, however, was mitigated by the consideration that the Soviet Union would not have accepted a part in the Geneva conference had it not felt confident that its contributions would compare favorably with those of the other major participants. Very little was known at first hand of these contributions because the Russians had long been out of the international scene of science. The end of the Second World War and the beginning of the "cold war" did not actually cause their withdrawal from Western science, but stressed and crystallized it. From then on, the Russians entirely stopped publishing works in English-language journals. But then, Russian scientists had not been seen in any appreciable number outside their country for over twenty years. In the field of atomic science they had never appeared.

4 WHAT IS THIS ATOMIC SCIENCE?

One of the purposes of the Conference on the Peaceful Uses of Atomic Energy, and not the least important, was to correct the widespread belief that atomic energy and atomic bombs are synonymous, that only the destructive atom, and not the peaceful atom, can exist. The misbelief is more than understandable, since atomic energy and atomic bombs were revealed to the world on the same day, August 6 of 1945, in the same dreadful event, the destruction of Hiroshima.

In this country we like to remember that the birth of the atomic era occurred over two and a half years before Hiroshima, on the afternoon of December 2, 1942, when "man achieved the first self-sustaining chain reaction and thereby initiated the controlled release of nuclear energy." Thus is the event commemorated on a plaque at the entrance of Stagg Field, the football stadium at the University of Chicago, where the experiment was performed in a squash court under the west stands. In the word "controlled" rest the expectations for the future: the physicists who performed the experiment had learned how to make matter yield its inner energy, not in a flash explosion but in a quiet, regulated way; how to start the release of energy and how to stop it, according to their will.

The device in which the first self-sustaining chain reaction took place was called a pile because it was made of graphite bricks *piled up* in layers, among which there were chunks of uranium at suitable places. The pile was in the shape of a sphere flattened at the top, about twenty-six feet in diameter and almost high enough to reach the ceiling of the squash court. It was built, and the experiment of making it chain-react was performed, under the direction of Dr. Enrico Fermi.

For this achievement Fermi has sometimes been called the "Architect of the Atomic Age." It cannot be overstressed, however, that a discovery, or a forward step on the path of knowledge, can never be attributed entirely to a single person or to a single group of persons. Science is an international enterprise and the result of many efforts coming one after the other, each adding impact to the results of the previous ones. The group of physicists who in wartime and in secrecy, almost in isolation, operated the first pile and made it yield atomic energy could not have done this without the previous work of other scientists. Before energy could be freed from uranium nuclei in Chicago, uranium fission had to be discovered. Before Hahn and Strassmann could achieve uranium fission in Berlin, artificial radioactivity had to be discovered. Before Irene Curie and her husband Frédéric Joliot Curie could discover it in Paris, the structure of the atom and the nature of its components had to be ascertained. The chain of scientific events could be traced back, zigzagging without interruption from one country to another, to the time when the first philosophers started speculating about nature.

So development of nuclear science cannot be attributed to a single person or to a single country. In this science the prime agent and factotum carrying the full load of the work is not a man but an elementary particle devoid of any national allegiance—the neutron. Ten years before the experiment in the squash court, the neutron had not yet been discovered. It remained elusive, although its existence had long been postulated by scientists in England, in the United States, and in Canada. On the basis of work done in France and in Germany, an Englishman finally detected it: James Chadwick, who later became Sir James and received the Nobel Prize for this discovery.

The neutron is one of the bricks of which all atoms, and consequently all matter, are built. Protons and electrons, the other atomic constituents, were known long before the neutrons. Two main reasons may account for the late discovery of neutrons: first, unlike protons and electrons, they carry no electrical charge and are not detected electrically with regular Geiger counters and ionization chambers; second, neutrons stay very much at home inside atomic nuclei, and it is difficult to get them to leave.

From the time of their discovery neutrons have been used to bombard atomic nuclei and cause their disintegration. Long and painstaking research was devoted to determining the nature of the new nuclei formed in this process. Particularly puzzling were the products of disintegration of uranium, some of which were not identified for several years. Finally in 1939 Hahn and Strassmann in Berlin discovered a phenomenon that shed light on the behavior of uranium: they observed that under neutron bombardment some uranium nuclei split in two almost equal parts. Atoms had been known to emit light particles, like electrons, protons, and alpha particles, but not to divide in fragments as big as half the uranium nucleus. This phenomenon was called fission. Fission is not just another nuclear process, another mode of atomic disintegration. Unique features make it of the greatest significance; when it occurs, the large amounts of energy that were holding the two parts of the uranium nucleus together are released, and neutrons are freed.

The importance of the energy release is evident. That of the production of neutrons needs some explanation. Suppose, for the sake of simplicity, that when a uranium nucleus undergoes fission two neutrons are liberated. We start with one neutron; this hits a uranium nucleus, releases energy and frees two neutrons; if each of these splits a uranium nucleus and frees two neutrons, there will then be four neutrons. These may induce fission in four uranium nuclei liberating eight neutrons. The process could thus go on by itself, in a chain reaction, and at each step the number of neutrons available to produce fission would double. In a very short time a huge number of nuclei would be undergoing fission, each surrendering its inner energy. Although in practical units the amount of energy from each uranium nucleus is very small, the total amount of energy from all the nuclei undergoing fission would be quite appreciable. The complete fission of one gram of uranium would release approximately twenty thousand kilowatt-hours, or sufficient energy to keep twenty thousand common electric bulbs lighted for ten hours.

In reality, between two and three neutrons are liberated in the fission of each uranium nucleus, yet fission, as observed in the laboratories, caused no chain reaction. The reason is simple: most of the neutrons generated did not produce further fission but escaped from the uranium or were lost as a result of other causes. When more neutrons are lost than created, a chain reaction cannot take place.

The Chicago pile was in substance a device contrived to make a sufficient number of neutrons do their duty—split uranium nuclei and sustain a chain reaction. With the progress of nuclear science other piles were built of different shape and design; the term *pile* was not always appropriate and was replaced by the more general term *reactor*. It was stated that there can be as many reactor designs as there are inventive minds; yet the same general principles of the original pile apply to all reactors, the main role of which is still to save as many neutrons as possible for the process of fission and its consequent release of energy.

When the Chicago pile was built, only natural uranium was available. This contains 140 parts of uranium of atomic weight 238 and one part of uranium of atomic weight 235. Unfortunately, only the least abundant isotope, U-235 undergoes fission appreciably. This statement, though not entirely correct, for U-238 may undergo fission under certain circumstances, is sufficiently accurate for the purpose of this discussion; in these pages we shall follow the general usage and consider U-238 as non-fissionable. Thus in the Chicago pile only a very small portion of the uranium could undergo fission and be utilized as nuclear fuel.

The neutrons emitted in fission are fast neutrons, which fly away at a great speed. The graphite in the Chicago pile had the function of slowing down the fast neutrons to a speed at which they were much more effective in hitting nuclei of U-235 and making them split. Graphite, or any other substance used for the purpose of slowing down neutrons is called a *moderator*. Once the neutrons are slowed down they are not only better at producing fission but are also more easily captured by U-238. This fact was bad for the Chicago pile, in which the neutron economy was very precarious, because the neutrons absorbed by U-238 were no longer available to produce fission in U-235. Once the chain reaction was achieved, this fact was no longer bad: when a U-238 nucleus captures a neutron, it undergoes a series of nuclear reactions and transforms into the nucleus of a new substance, plutonium. And plutonium is fissionable.

The capture of neutrons by U-238 was not the only cause of neutron losses that had to be taken into account in the construction of the Chicago pile. Some neutrons might escape out of the pile and others might be absorbed by impurities. To reduce the loss caused by impurities, both uranium and graphite were made pure to a degree that had not been attempted before. To reduce the loss by escape, the pile was made very large: had it been small, the neutrons would have found their way out more easily, before they had a chance of being properly slowed down and of encountering a nucleus of U-235 in their path. The physicists who built the pile had gone on adding graphite bricks and chunks of uranium until the neutrons generated by fission balanced the losses due to all causes. The size at which this balance occurs in a nuclear device is called *critical size*. Once the critical size is reached, the chain reaction can sustain itself for a while, but when some of the fuel is burned, and not enough of it is left to regenerate as many neutrons as are lost, the device becomes subcritical. Thus, in order to maintain the chain reaction, the size of a nuclear device must be somewhat larger than its critical size.

Neutrons are easily absorbed by many substances, and this property, which may constitute a difficulty as in the case of impurities, was put to good use to control the reaction in the Chicago pile. For this purpose the pile was equipped with a rod of cadmium, which is a good neutron absorber. When this rod was inserted inside the pile, it absorbed a large quantity of neutrons, and the chain reaction could not take place. If part of the rod was pulled out, the number of neutrons that it absorbed decreased, and the number of those available for fission increased. At a certain position of the rod, a balance was achieved between neutrons lost from all causes, including absorption by the cadmium rod, and neutrons generated in fission. At this point the chain reaction became self-sustaining and went on at a steady rate. If the rod was pulled out further, the rate of propagation of the chain reaction and consequently the rate of energy release increased. The increase could be stopped, and the pile could be operated at the new level, by reinserting the cadmium rod to the correct position.

The Chicago pile was not built to develop useful power but to demonstrate that a chain reaction was feasible and to study the pile's behavior. It was kept as simple as possible and therefore was not provided with a coolant to remove the heat generated in fission or with a shielding to protect the personnel from radioactivity. For this reason it was operated at the very low power of half a watt the first day, of two hundred watts a few days later, and heat and radioactivity were produced in unimportant amounts.

Reactor technology has progressed much. It is now possible to "enrich" natural uranium, increasing the percentage of the more fissionable isotope U-235, through a separation process. Because the two isotopes are chemically almost identical, the separation cannot be achieved by ordinary chemical processes but must be based on their principal difference, atomic weight. Several methods of enriching uranium were devised, one of which, the gaseous diffusion method, is used on a large scale. The idea is simple: when a mixture of gases of different atomic weight diffuses through a porous barrier, the lighter components pass at a faster rate than the heavier. Natural uranium, which normally is a heavy metallic substance, can form a gas if combined with fluorine. When uranium hexafluoride goes through a suitable porous substance, the hexafluoride containing U-235 diffuses just a bit faster than that containing U-238. If the diffusion is stopped when only part of the gas has gone through the porous barrier, that part will contain a slightly higher proportion of U-235 than the part left behind. The increase in U-235 is very small, but, if the process is repeated by letting the gas go through many successive barriers, it is possible to obtain the desired enrichment.

It is easy to build a reactor with enriched uranium: there is much less U-238 to capture neutrons and the neutron economy is greatly improved. Impurities become less important, and substances other than graphite can be used as moderator: water, for instance, is plentiful and cheap. Like graphite, it slows down neutrons, but it also absorbs a few of them. If enriched uranium can be had, who cares about some losses? The chain reaction can take place all the same.

On the other hand, in the design of operating reactors, engineering problems that did not exist in the Chicago pile arise from the fact that heat and radiations are produced. Heat must be removed from the fuel, by means of a *coolant*, which may be a gas or a liquid, water for instance, or even a liquid metal. Fuel must be accessible to the coolant, and consequently it is not scattered around in big "chunks" but is usually fabricated into fuel elements, which are also more easily handled and can be withdrawn from the reactor if the need arises. If the fuel elements are placed close to one another, they form the reactor core. In some reactors the fuel is dissolved in a liquid, which may act also as moderator, or even as moderator and coolant. The neutrons that try to escape out of the reactor are intercepted by a *reflector* and directed back toward the fuel.

To protect the personnel from radioactivity, modern reactors are provided with shielding which may consist of great thicknesses of concrete inclosing the entire reactor. In "swimming pool" reactors, that wonderful substance, water, is also used for this purpose: the reactor core is immersed in water, which acts as moderator, reflector, coolant, and shielding. Water used for shielding makes the reactor entirely visible, a feature which is very useful, particularly in the case of reactors for research.

If electricity is to be produced, the heat developed in the fuel is carried by the coolant to a heat exchanger, where it produces steam. The steam can be made to operate a turbine.

The electricity that will be produced in atomic power plants in the next few years will be more expensive than that generated by conventional methods. It may not always be so. There is a prospect that makes the physicists' eyes shine when they mention it, the ambitious goal to make use of the *breeding* principle. Breeding, they say, is the real reason for reactors, the justification of all efforts that have gone and will go into the development of reactor technology. In their enthusiasm they may forget to say what breeding means: to produce more fuel than is burned and to do this as the fuel is being burned, in the same reactor.

This is not as impossible a feat as it sounds. It has already been mentioned that when U-238 absorbs neutrons it transforms into plutonium, which is fissionable. Thus a peculiarity of nuclear fuel is that, in burning, it may create some new fuel. Whether more can be created than burned is a question of neutron economy. In a chain reaction one neutron from each fission must produce a new fission, or the reaction will stop; any extra neutrons can theoretically convert U-238 into plutonium. In practice a few are always lost. Yet, since in each fission between two and three neutrons are liberated, it is conceivable that more than one may be utilized to manufacture plutonium, producing more than one atom of it for each burned atom of U-235. Another element, thorium, can absorb neutrons and transform into fissionable U-233; so thorium can be used to breed fuel.

Breeder reactors are being studied, both in the United States and in England, and have been achieved on an experimental scale. They consist of a core of fissionable material, U-235 or plutonium, and they are surrounded by a *blanket* of thorium, or natural or depleted uranium, in which the new fuel is generated. Many difficult engineering problems are still to be solved, but the outlook for achieving breeding in large power plants is bright. Then it will be possible to extract a great part of the energy contained in the large quantities of uranium that exist in nature. If breeding is achieved, one ton of uranium may do the work of three or four million tons of coal.

In this brief discussion of the chain reaction and of chain-reacting devices we have considered uranium nuclei and neutrons, but we have overlooked the two fragments into which a uranium nucleus splits when it undergoes fission.

It is now time to consider these and see how they affect the operation of reactors. When uranium nuclei undergo fission they always divide in two parts of comparable mass; but these two parts are not always the same. Fission may occur in at least thirty different modes, each giving origin to a different pair of fragments. Thus over sixty different substances are directly formed from uranium during fission. These substances are radioactive and they disintegrate, some rapidly and some slowly, forming still other substances. Thus nuclear fuel in which a chain reaction has taken place for some time contains many fission products, some of which are good neutron absorbers. As reactor operation proceeds and fission products increase in quantity, they absorb so many neutrons that not enough are left to maintain the chain reaction. The fuel is said to be "poisoned." Fission products must be removed, much as cinders must be shaken off the coal in a common furnace. Removal of fission products is, however, a much more difficult operation than the shaking of a grate. It cannot be performed inside the reactor. The fuel elements must be removed, with suitable precautions, for the fission products make them highly radioactive, and they must be replaced with new ones. In special reprocessing plants the fissionable material that still remains in the spent fuel elements is separated from the fission products and used in the fabrication of new fuel elements.

Fission products, which hinder reactor operations, are quite useful once they are extracted from the fuel. They contain many isotopes, both stable and radioactive, which have found very important applications, as we shall see shortly.

In considering the peaceful uses of atomic energy, there is a tendency to place the emphasis on production of power, but the greatest benefits realized so far have come from the use of radioactive isotopes. A day may well come in the future when all our industries will use electricity generated in atomic power plants, when our cities will be lighted by atomic energy. For the present these are dreams, or at best well-grounded expectations. The few power plants under construction or being planned in several countries, in a program that is still in the experimental stage, will provide only a very small fraction of the power consumption of the world.

Radioisotopes, on the other hand, are already bringing returns. In United States industry their use has resulted in savings estimated at one hundred million dollars a year, and it is expected to grow rapidly. They hold great promise for agriculture, where their use is already bringing financial gains. Their achievements in the fields of biology and medicine cannot be measured in money; radioisotopes are used successfully in medical treatment and diagnosis; and, what may well be more important than any of their other feats, they have furthered rapid progress in the understanding of the basic processes of life.

Natural uranium contains two isotopes which are chemically indistinguishable and differ in their atomic weight. In a similar way, many elements are a mixture of two or more isotopes, chemically indistinguishable from one another but having a slightly different atomic weight. Most of the naturally occurring isotopes are stable, and only those of the heavy elements at the end of the periodic system are radioactive. In nuclear reactors radioisotopes of many of the lighter elements are created in large quantities.

Radioactive substances were used both in medical therapy and in research long before reactors began producing large quantities of radioisotopes. Natural radioactivity was discovered in 1896 by Henri Becquerel, and two years later Marie and Pierre Curie identified radium and several other radioactive elements. It was thought at once that the radiations emitted by radium would destroy living cells, and, in particular, cancerous tissues. Small amounts of radium were soon used in the treatment of some forms of cancer. Naturally occurring radioactive substances are scarce and costly. In order to obtain one gram of radium from the richest pitchblende, several tons of this mineral must be treated.

Artificial radioactivity was discovered by Irene Curie, Marie's daughter, and her husband Frédéric Joliot Curie at the end of 1933. They were bombarding aluminum with alpha particles when they noticed that under this bombardment some of the aluminum nuclei emitted one proton each and transformed into radioactive nuclei of phosphorus. Radiophosphorus was the first man-made radioisotope. Radioactivity was induced in a few other light elements by bombardment with alpha particles, but the amounts of radioactive substances produced were infinitesimal, and no practical use could be foreseen for them.

In 1934, Enrico Fermi and his collaborators in Rome used neutrons instead of alpha particles and succeeded in activating a large number of elements. In the course of these studies they discovered that certain light substances interposed between the neutrons and their target slowed down the neutrons and greatly increased their chances of being captured by the target substance. This is quite understandable if one thinks of the neutrons as balls and of the atoms as ball players in a field: if the balls are slow the players will catch them more easily and in larger numbers than if they zoom by at great speed.

Up to a hundred times larger quantities of radioactive isotopes were produced with slow than with fast neutrons or with alpha particles. Yet a hundred times an infinitesimal quantity is still a submicroscopic amount which can be recognized only by means of counters and similar radiation detectors. For practical purposes the achievements of slow neutrons seemed negligible.

Ernest Lawrence, in Berkeley, California, tried a different kind of nuclar projectile with better success: with deuterons accelerated in his cyclotron he obtained radioactive isotopes of almost all elements, in quantities comparable to those of the natural radioactive substances available at that time. A large variety of radioactive isotopes was placed at the disposal of research, and scientists in many fields took immediate advantage of them, although the price was still high. Lawrence's method seemed by far the most promising.

Slow neutrons, and not the cyclotron, led to truly abundant and economical production of radioisotopes; the study of the artificial radioactivity induced in uranium by slow neutrons, undertaken in Rome, was pursued also in Berlin. There Hahn and Strassmann discovered uranium fission, which made possible the realization of chain reaction and reactors.

Cyclotrons may produce a wider variety of radioisotopes, but reactors yield them in far larger amounts and can make many different ones at the same time. Many useful radioisotopes are found among the fission products, and others can be obtained by exposing various substances to bombardment by the neutrons inside a reactor.

Radioisotopes can be used in two main broad ways: as sources of radiations and as "tracers." In cancer treatment by radium, radium is used as a source of radiations; these enter the cancerous tissues and destroy their cells. When Irene Curie and her husband discovered artificial radioactivity, their nuclear projectiles were alpha particles emitted spontaneously by polonium. In their experiment polonium was used as a source of alpha radiation. Some of the radioisotopes are excellent sources of gamma rays, which are electromagnetic waves similar to X-rays. These radioisotopes can be used instead of X-ray machines, both for treatment and to make radiographs. During the last few years many teletherapy cobalt units were installed in hospitals all over the United States and in other countries. They contain large amounts of radioactive cobalt 60 made in nuclear reactors, and give out a beam of gamma rays as penetrating as that from a two- to three-million-volt X-ray machine. Radiocobalt units are much cheaper to buy and operate, are more compact, steadier, and easier to handle than million volt X-ray machines.

The use of radioisotopes as tracers and the kind of problems they may help to solve were aptly illustrated by Senator Clinton P. Anderson, Chairman of the Joint Committee on Atomic Energy, in an address before the Rotary Club of Albuquerque, New Mexico, on May 31, 1955. Here is his most amusing example:

"If you believe," he said, "your wife isn't getting the breakfast dishes clean, test how well she does her work. You merely feed some radioactive phosphorus to chickens who lay radioactive eggs; your wife fries eggs; you eat them but leave a little egg on the dish; she washes the plate and you check [with a counter] to see if radioactive material remains. . . . That's the way a dishwasher manufacturer tested the efficiency of . . . a new dishwasher. . . . Radioisotopes did the job by finding traces of dried fried egg on a plate— and if you want to test it in this modern way at home, I can supply the isotopes and can guarantee you'll either get a new dishwasher or a new wife, but you'll be doing it on a scientific basis."

A change of wife is not a necessary step in the tracer technique. The essential fact is that radioactive phosphorus was used to "label" the eggs, which acquired the distinctive feature of sending off radiations. They could have been identified as the ones laid by the chicken fed with radioactive phosphorus, even if mixed with dozens of other eggs. Once these eggs had been eaten, their digestion and assimilation could have been followed through the radioactivity of radiophosphorus. Radioactive phosphorus had mixed with the ordinary phosphorus that the chicken utilized to make eggs and had shared its fate.

In general, radioactive atoms of an element are chemically identical to ordinary or stable atoms of the element and they go along with them in all chemical and biochemical processes. But because they give off radiations they can be detected with counters and followed through these processes.

The tracer technique was first devised by Hevesy and Paneth in 1913, long before the discovery of artificial radioactivity. They used minute amounts of natural radioactive lead to study the solubility of lead salts. Hevesy was the first to apply radioactive tracers to biology: in 1923 he again labeled a lead salt with minute quantities of radioactive lead and investigated how solutions of this lead salt were taken up by plants. Other studies of absorption of nutrients by plants, studies which are of great importance to agriculture, were initiated by Hevesy and a collaborator, using radioactive phosphorus. The use of radiophosphorus has permitted the labeling of fertilizers and the determination of what proportion of the phosphorus absorbed by a plant comes from the soil and what from the added fertilizer.

In medicine, tracers have been and are invaluable both as re-

At the first meeting of the Advisory Committee Dr. I. I. Rabi (left), representing the United States, greets Dr. Dmitri V. Skobeltzin of the Soviet Union. Standing between them is Dr. J. V. Dunworth of the United Kingdom

The President and the six Vice-Presidents of the Conference. From left to right: *W. B. Lewis (Canada); Francis Perrin (France); I. I. Rabi (United States); Homi J. Bhabha (India), Conference President; D. V. Skobeltzin (U.S.S.R.); John D. Cockcroft (United Kingdom); Bernardino de Mattos (Brazil)*

No. 486 — St. Paul's Hospital, Vancouver, and Nurses' Residence, Greater Vancouver

On the platform of the Assembly Hall, at the opening session of the Conference.
From left to right: *Mr. Max Petitpierre, President of the Swiss Confederation;
Mr. Dag Hammarskjöld, Secretary-General of the United Nations; Dr. Homi J.
Bhabha of India, President of the Conference; and Professor Walter G. Whitman,
Conference Secretary-General*

*Admiral Lewis L. Strauss, Chairman of the
United States Atomic Energy Commission
and of the United States Delegation to the
Conference, speaks to the press at Geneva*

Commercial exhibits in the Palais des Expositions

Opening session in the Assembly Hall

A model of a British power plant at the commercial exhibit arouses the public interest

Distribution of United Nations Conference documents at the Palais des Nations

Rest between sessions in the halls of the Palais des Nations

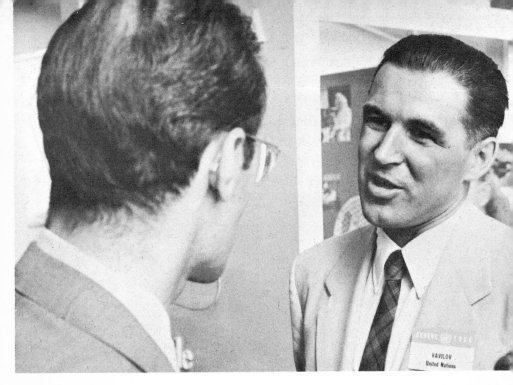

Dr. Viktor S. Vavilov, Deputy Conference Secretary-General, chats with a friend at the French exhibits

A Russian interpreter (right) *and two Russian scientists at the U.S.S.R. exhibits ponder over questions asked by Dr. Walter H. Zinn, then Director of Argonne National Laboratory*

The crate containing the control panel for the Geneva reactor is loaded on the Globemaster at the Tyson McGhee Air Force Base

EXPORT LICENSE

FORM AEC 257
(6-49)

AEC LICENSE NO.

THIS LICENSE EXPIRES December 31, 1955

F - ᵒᵒᵒ2

United States of America
Atomic Energy Commission

LICENSEE	PURCHASER OR ULTIMATE CONSIGNEE IN FOREIGN COUNTRY
NAME U. S. Atomic Energy Commission 1901 Constitution Ave., N. W. ADDRESS Washington 25, D. C.	USAEC, Conference on Atomic Energy NAME c/o J. D. Conway, Overseas Manager Union Carbide Europa, S. A. ADDRESS 1-3, Rue de Chantepoulet Geneva, SWITZERLAND

APPLICANT'S REF. NO.	COUNTRY OF ULTIMATE DESTINATION	INTERMEDIATE CONSIGNEE IN FOREIGN COUNTRY
—	SWITZERLAND	NAME SAME ADDRESS

QUANTITY	DESCRIPTION OF MATERIAL	UNIT PRICE	TOTAL PRICE
---40 Crates	(Approx.)- Components and accessories for a Nuclear Reactor	. . . . .	$207,857.00
NOTE:	Shipment is to be accompanied by Mr. David F. Cope.		

///END//

Not valid unless signed by licensee on the REVERSE

Pursuant to the Atomic Energy Act of 1954 and Section 50.21 of Title 10, Code of Federal Regulations, Chapter I, Part 50- Control of Facilities for the Production of Fissionable Material, and in reliance on statements and representations heretofore made by the licensee, a license is hereby issued to the licensee authorizing the manufacture and production for export, and/or transfer for export, or acquisition for export, and export of the facilities listed above, subject to the terms and provisions herein. The license to export extends to the licensee's duly authorized shipping agent.

THIS LICENSE IS INVALID UNLESS SIGNED BELOW
BY AUTHORIZED AEC REPRESENTATIVE

FOR THE U.S. ATOMIC ENERGY COMMISSION

AUTHORIZED AEC REPRESENTATIVE

JUN 27 1955

EXPORT LICENSE

The first export license ever issued for a reactor

George H. Manov

SIGNATURE OF LICENSEE
Atomic Energy Commission
1901 Constitution Ave , Washington, D.C.

ADDRESS

COLLECTORS OF CUSTOMS OR POSTMASTERS WILL ENDORSE IN THE FOLLOWING SPACE INFORMATION
CONCERNING EACH SHIPMENT MADE UNDER THIS LICENSE

QUANTITY	DESCRIPTION OF MATERIAL

Visitors stand in line in front of the chalet housing the United States reactor

At a party. From left, on foreground: *Dr. I. I. Rabi, United States; Dr. Ralph J. Bunche and Mr. Dag Hammarskjöld of the United Nations*

Reactor school for guides. Mr. Roy Clark (left) *and Dr. François Kertesz* (right) *are the teachers*

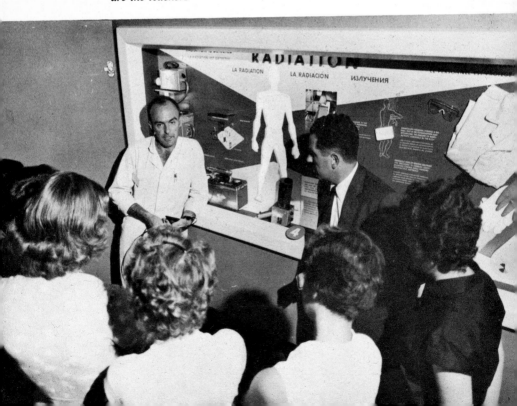

Professor Otto Hahn of Germany (left) with Professor and Mrs. Niels Bohr

Dr. Homi J. Bhabha, Conference President, pushes the button and operates the Geneva reactor, watched by Dr. Walter G. Whitman, Conference Secretary-General

At the Geneva reactor: the general public

At the Geneva reactor: a group of Russian scientists

Workers at the Geneva Conference, on the top of the Palais des Nations. From left to right: *Russian biologist; United States historian; Russian mineralogist; director of French exhibits; interpreter; British worker at exhibits; Russian chemist; Irish worker at exhibits*

Russian exhibits. To the left is the model of the U.S.S.R. atomic power station

An interpreter at the Russian exhibits explains results of biological research to a group of visitors. To his right is Secretary-General Dag Hammarskjöld of the United Nations

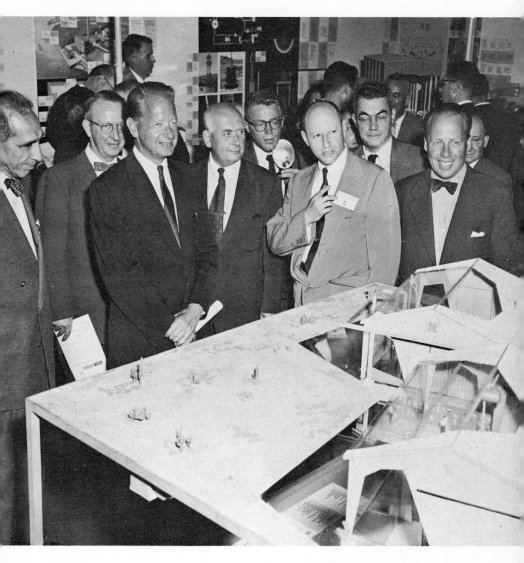

Dr. George L. Weil, Technical Director of the United States Delegation, explains the model of an atomic station to a group of United Nations officials at the United States Technical Exhibits. To his left, in the front row, holding a rolled-up paper, is Secretary-General Dag Hammarskjöld

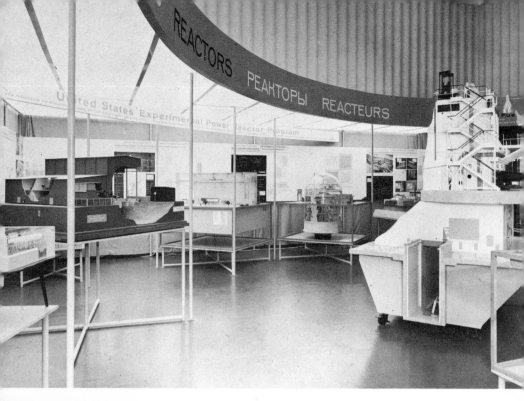

Models of reactors at the United States Technical Exhibits

United States Technical Exhibits: Section on Radiation and Plant Genetics

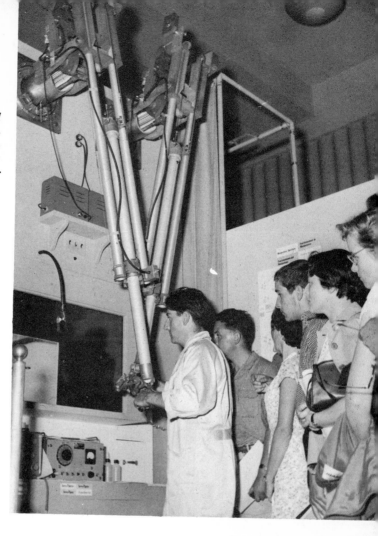

A scientist at the United States Technical Exhibits demonstrates the use of "magic hands" for remote handling of radioactive substances

Delegates of many countries visit the United States Technical Exhibits

The United States Technical Library

Professor Veksler, of Russia, reads a scientific paper

Ex-Premier Mario Scelba (left) and Professor Francesco Giordani (right), head of the Italian Delegation, collect illustrative pamphlets at technical exhibits of various countries

At an evening lecture Dr. Willard F. Libby shows a 2,000-year-old piece of rope and a 9,000-year-old slipper dated with the radioactive-carbon method

Admiral Strauss signs the agreement transferring the Geneva reactor to the Swiss. Sitting by him are Mr. Walter Boveri of the Swiss "Reacteur," S.A., and Miss Frances E. Willis, United States Ambassador to Switzerland

search and as diagnostic tools. It may be of medical interest, for instance, to know the rate at which sodium travels in a patient's body. Ordinarily there would be no way of telling what happens to sodium once it is ingested, for its atoms are in all respects identical to those of sodium present in the body. But if the patient is given common salt (sodium chloride) that has been irradiated so as to contain radioactive sodium, the path of the sodium can be followed along the body with a counter held outside it. This method is applied to diagnose cases of defective blood circulation: a small quantity of a solution of labeled salt is injected into the vein of the patient's arm; a Geiger counter is then placed in contact with one of his feet; if blood circulation is normal, the counter will soon detect radioactivity, which will increase rapidly. If there is some impairment in the circulation, the radioactivity will increase slowly, showing that the blood has difficulty reaching the foot in contact with the counter. By moving the counter to different parts of the body, the position of the restriction can be located.

Salt containing radiosodium can be obtained by exposing ordinary salt to the neutrons inside a reactor, but labeled compounds cannot always be obtained by this simple method. It is in order at this point to return to Senator Anderson's radioactive egg and give it some deeper consideration. Senator Anderson did not suggest that the husband doubting his wife's efficiency try to label the egg himself. How could he do it? He would not want to irradiate the whole egg and ingest that much radioactivity. Besides, who could tell what the taste and the consistency of the irradiated egg would be? The only way to attach a label to the content of the egg was to let the chicken do the job. There are many instances in which it is not possible to label an organic compound in the laboratory, and so the task is passed on to animals and plants, which attach the desired label while performing the *biosynthesis* of the compound. Acetic acid containing radioactive carbon can be obtained by biosynthesis, using certain bacteria. If this radioactive acetic acid is given to a pig, radioactive cholesterol will be found in the pig's blood. Cholesterol is a substance present in all animals. Its role in arteriosclerosis and in cancer is being investigated. Radioactive cholesterol makes these investigations possible.

In a similar way, plants grown in the presence of radioactive carbon dioxide will yield labeled products: sugar beets will manufacture labeled sugar; tobacco plants will manufacture labeled nicotine; poppy plants, radioactive morphine. Thus an array of labeled drugs can be prepared for studying their action, the rate at which they are absorbed, the tissues where they are deposited. The doctor of the future may well carry an assortment of radioactive pills in his bag.

When Senator Anderson offered to furnish the radiophosphorus for the egg experiment, he should have cautioned the men in the audience to feed it to the chicken as soon as they received it and not to wait too long to eat the labeled egg once it had been laid. The activity of the radiophosphorus decays rather rapidly; in about fourteen days it becomes one-half of what it was at the start and in a few weeks it may become too weak to be detected. In scientific terminology it is said that the *half-life* of radiophosphorus is 14.3 days. The half-life of a radioisotope is defined as the time required for the radioactivity of a given amount of the isotope to decay to half its initial value.

The half-life is a characteristic of each isotope, and its value for the various substances varies over an enormous range: the half-life of uranium is four and a half billion years, while that of some radioactive substances is only a very small fraction of a second. Thus, in selecting radioisotopes to be used as tracers, their half-life must be taken into account. Some, with a short half-life, may decay too fast for many experiments. Those with a long half-life, on the other hand, are less active and may emit weaker radiations, which may be difficult to detect.

Tracer isotopes have been called the most important research tool to be developed since the microscope. The microscope has made it possible to see individual cells, to understand their relations and the constitution of tissues. Isotopes permit the examination of the chemical and biological activities that lead to the formation of those cells and tissues, of the exchanges between the constituents of a living organism and the substances that it absorbs. Many old views about the utilization of carbohydrates, proteins, and fats were revised in the light of results of investigations with tracers. It was ascertained that in the animal body there is a continuous exchange between the substances supplied in the diet and those already present in animal tissues, including bones and teeth, and in the course of time the body undergoes almost complete renewal.

The synthesis of the basic substances inside a living organism is under study, and much information in this field has been accumulated. Extensive work with tracers has been directed at the interpretation of photosynthesis, the process by which green plants convert carbon, hydrogen, and oxygen into energy-containing carbohydrates. It was known that the process took place in the presence of sunlight and of chlorophyll, the green coloring matter of plants. The role of chlorophyll and light was not understood, and the study of the successive steps in the process seemed impossible until the advent of isotopes provided a particularly suitable tool and gave an incentive to renewed investigations of the mechanism of photosynthesis.

In the field of industry and technology the applications of radioisotopes have spread very fast and seem to be limited only by human inventiveness. They are so varied that a review of them, even on broad lines, is not possible here, and only a few examples will be briefly mentioned.

In industry, as in biology, radioisotopes can be used as tracers or as sources of radiation. In the oil industry, for instance, many tracer techniques are now part of routine operations. In transcontinental pipelines different kinds of oils are sent successively through the same pipe. To avoid waste, it is necessary to know exactly when the boundary between two different products arrives at the receiving end so that they may be switched to different tanks. This may be done by injecting a small amount of a radioisotope at the boundary and using a counter at the receiving end to detect its arrival. Tracers are used to solve other problems connected with transportation and extraction of oil: a suspension of radioactive particles may be pumped into a well and the radioactivity may be logged along its length, revealing leaks, open formations, and permeable zones. A radioactive tracer added to the oil of an underground pipeline will make it possible to detect leaks with a counter above ground, without the need for extensive digging along the line.

Tracers are used also for wear tests: in the case of metal parts, like engine piston rings, the part itself is irradiated and made radioactive; when the part is being tested, small radioactive amounts of metal particles will go into the lubricating oil. From the radioactivity in the oil it is possible to measure the wear of the part much more rapidly than by other means. In other cases, for instance in tests of tires, a labeling isotope is added to the material of which the part is made, in this instance to the rubber that will go into the tire. When this tire is run over a testing surface, small particles of rubber will adhere to the surface. From the amount of radioactivity on the surface it is possible to detect and calculate the very small amount of rubber lost by the tire.

Larger quantities of radioisotopes are used in industry as sources of radiation than as tracers. Isotopes emitting beta rays are employed in the beta-ray thickness gauge: the radioisotope is placed on one side of the material, which is usually in sheet form; a radiation detector is placed on the other side. The greater the thickness, the more rays are absorbed; and thus, from the reading of the detector the thickness can be measured. Thickness gauges have been widely used in making sheets of metal, plastic, paper, cloth, and floor covering; they cannot only detect variations in thickness but also can be built to control automatically the setting of the rollers rolling out the sheet.

For the sake of those readers to whom these few industrial applications of radioisotopes appear too specific and limited in scope, we shall mention one much broader use, now under study, which may soon bring results affecting all our homes: the processing of food by radiation sterilization. Exposure to moderate amounts of radiation destroys bacteria in fresh food, without raising its temperature. This has been called the first promising new principle of food sterilization since Nicholas Appert discovered the art of canning in 1809.

The housewife who has remorsefully thrown an occasional half-loaf of moldy bread in the garbage may look forward to the time when bread will not mold in even the muggiest weather. Relief organizations that could not ship potatoes overseas because they sprouted and deteriorated too fast may hope that in a not too distant future potatoes will not sprout and will keep their appearance unchanged for as long as two years and more. Perhaps meat will be kept on shelves, out of the freezer, and all "canned" foods will become "packaged" foods, since it will be no longer necessary that containers be resistant to heat and pressure. Unfortunately radiations alter the taste or the color of some foods, like milk, and only patient research may succeed in overcoming this difficulty. In any case, whether there are apparent alterations or not, before radiation-processed foods can be recommended for large-scale consumption, it must be proved beyond doubt that they are not made toxic by radiation and that their nutritional value is not reduced considerably.

Extensive investigations are being pursued in this field by scientists and food experts with the co-operation and under the direction of the United States Army's Office of the Quartermaster General. The Army needs to feed large groups and often must transport food for great distances. Any simplification of transportation and storage of food would therefore benefit the Army.

Early in 1956, Dr. Libby estimated possible Army savings in a speech before the Conference on Radioactive Isotopes in Agriculture in East Lansing, Michigan. He said: "The Armed Forces purchases almost $2 billion per year in perishables, among which are two and three-quarters billion pounds of fresh meat and three-quarter billion pounds of canned meat. Refrigeration costs for the Armed Forces are estimated at $40/man/year. If radiation preservation of perishable foods can be successfully achieved and one-fourth of this amount is saved per year, a two million man army would represent potential savings of $20 million per year."

The previous pages have given the bright side of the picture, the promises of atomic energy: power, knowledge, and progress. And now the reader must take a glance at the reverse side.

Radiations are dangerous. Large amounts of radiations are extremely dangerous. The radioactivity due to fission products in the spent fuel elements of a nuclear reactor is many thousand times greater than that due to all the radium extracted in the last fifty years. With the increase in power and in number of reactors, much larger amounts of radiations will be produced. Even work with small amounts of radioactivity, like tracer studies, involves some danger. We are all conditioned to expect pain as a warning signal of potential harm to our health. Pain makes us withdraw our hands from objects sufficiently hot to injure our tissues. In the case of radiation there is no such signal, and the effects of exposure may not appear for weeks. Thus a worker has no way of telling subjectively whether he is being exposed to harmful quantities of radiation or, for that matter, whether he is being exposed at all. Only objective measurement will provide the answer.

The responsibility for studying, and insuring protection of personnel against, radiation hazards has been placed in the hands of new specialists, the health physicists. They have set standards for safe levels of exposure to different types of radiation; they have contrived means for detecting and measuring radiations under various conditions; they have developed suitable protection methods. The continuous check on radiation in places where radioactive material is handled is called *monitoring*, which is divided into the monitoring of personnel and of the area. Monitoring of personnel is achieved with film badges or other radiation detectors worn by each worker and checked at the end of an established time, usually a week; they show the total amount of radiation to which the worker has been exposed during that time. Other instruments may indicate at any time whether a worker is carrying radioactivity on his hands or shoes. Monitoring of the space where work with radioactive materials is performed is done with various types of fixed and portable instruments. Some measure continuously the activity present in the air inside buildings; others are used in special places when a particularly dangerous operation is carried on. Several of these instruments automatically send off a signal if the radiation intensity exceeds the tolerance level.

The protection of personnel is obtained by shielding radiation sources and remote handling of radioactive substances. Reactors are inclosed in protective shieldings; radioisotopes are shipped in heavy lead containers which absorb the radiations; "hot" parts of buildings are separated by heavy lead doors from those parts where no radiation is handled. A new technology has developed for the remote handling of dangerous material: fuel elements are removed from a reactor by mechanical devices operated from a distance; new instruments permit working on substances under great depths of water, which absorbs radiations; with "magic hands" the modern researcher can perform delicate analysis and chemical operations in laboratories which he need not enter and from which he is separated by thick lead walls and thick windows.

Not all the fission products formed in a reactor are suitable for constructive use, and a large part of them are waste. The problem of their disposal is one to which much attention has been and is being given. Some of these wastes are short-lived, and after they are stored for a certain time their radioactivity has sufficiently decayed to cease being a health hazard. The long-lived components must be disposed of in such a way that they do not endanger man or his environment. They cannot be discharged into waters that are ultimately used to irrigate fields where plants are grown for human consumption, or into soil where they may be dragged along by underground water to places where plants may absorb them: the plants would contain radioactivity and, if eaten by men or by animals successively eaten by men, the radioactivity would be transferred into the human body, with harmful effects. The same reasoning is valid for fishing waters. The gases coming from fission products or from gas-cooled reactors cannot be let out in the air without special precautions which include decontamination of the gas and tall stacks to discharge the gas high above the ground.

Despite all precautions, widespread use of atomic power may cause a significant increase of the radiation level in the atmosphere. The human race has always been subjected to a low level of natural radiation from cosmic rays and from radioactive elements contained in the earth, and geneticists believe that part of the spontaneous mutations that have occurred and are occurring in the human race are due to this radiation. Any increase in the radiation level may increase the number of mutations and thus affect our future generations. How and how much is not known. Long and painstaking studies are needed before the genetic effects of radiation in mankind are fully understood.

5 GENEVA

During the last ten days of July the Office for the International Conference was moved from Washington to Geneva. When the first OIC people arrived, the Big Four meeting was drawing to an end, and its success was already assured. The change of spirit that President Eisenhower had set as the aim of the conference had become reality, at least temporarily. The chiefs of the governments of France, England, the United States, and the Soviet Union had sat together around conference and dinner tables as friends: friends who had many divergencies of opinion but who could discuss them without mutual mistrust; who were willing to listen to each other's criticism; who seemed to have the same ultimate goal in mind— peaceful coexistence and the good of humanity. They had all professed a firm intention to avoid war, and their sincerity had not been questioned. Their talks had created an atmosphere of good will, harmony, and confidence, which to all appearances was there to stay. The "spirit of Geneva" was being hailed the world over. And the Big Four leaders were making ready to return to their countries.

The OIC people were more than relieved; they were rejoicing. If the political conference had been unsuccessful, it might have adversely affected the scientific conference. If it had been protracted— President Eisenhower had declared himself willing to stay in Geneva as long as profitable—shortage of space in Geneva might have delayed the moving of the OIC across the ocean. The Big Four meeting lasted six days instead of four, from July 18 to 23, but the two extra days did not appreciably upset the schedule of preparations for the scientific conference, and, what is more important, the friendliness, the spirit of co-operation that the political meeting left behind constituted as effective a background as one could possibly wish for the conference on the peaceful uses of atomic energy.

The OIC moved into the modern Hôtel du Rhône, where the United States Consulate had its permanent seat, and at first it occupied only those rooms that the Consulate kept for the use of United States missions to international meetings. None of our previous missions to Geneva had been as large as our technical delegation, and soon Mr. Franklin C. Gowen, the Consul-General, saw a never ceasing flow of people invade offices that he might have liked to keep for his staff and for his regular business. He submitted graciously, but after a while the space available through his courtesy was no longer sufficient to satisfy the increasing demands of the OIC.

After each bit of space in the Hôtel du Rhône had been filled, a nearby schoolhouse was taken over, and a good portion of the staff and of its files was moved there. Although the conference had not yet started, the files of the United States delegation were already so heavy that the plane on which they had been loaded for the flight across the ocean had been compelled to discharge part of them at Gander Airport in Newfoundland, where they had remained several days, waiting for a less burdened plane to pick them up.

At the very end of July, Mr. Gowen was worried: the housing unit, in charge of finding rooms for delegates, had received requests for five hundred beds and was one hundred short. The size of our mission to Geneva had grown considerably larger than early expectations. The official United States delegation, as it appeared in the "List of Delegates" distributed by the United Nations, reckoned 259 members. In compliance with the rules of procedure of the conference, our delegation had five official representatives: Admiral Lewis L. Strauss, whom President Eisenhower had appointed chairman of the delegation; Commissioner Willard F. Libby; Professor Isidor I. Rabi; Professor Detlev W. Bronk, president of the National Academy of Sciences; and Dr. Shields Warren, scientific director of the Cancer Institute at the New England Deaconess Hospital.

The rest of the delegates were advisers to the official representatives. There were four members of the Senate and four of the House of Representatives. One hundred and eighty-three of the advisers to the delegation were scientists, most of whom were to present papers; others were to give evening lectures or to chair one of the sessions. There were ten advisers from the Department of State. The rest of the members of the delegation and its secretariat included the staff of the OIC and other officials, of both the Atomic Energy Commission and the State Department, responsible for the organization and the functioning of our technical delegation. The 259 delegates did not include either the office secretaries of the OIC or the staffs of the technical library, the exhibits, and the reactor. Furthermore, many delegates had brought along their wives, and some, their children.

As the scientists who were to deliver papers at the conference arrived, they reported to Dr. Paul McDaniel and received last-minute directions. The United Nations scientific secretaries were continuously revising the program as they received late papers. They tried to have as many countries represented and as many scientists of each country present papers orally as possible. The program was crowded from the start, and, as the number of papers increased, the timing of each paper had to be adjusted with care. Paul McDaniel kept in touch with the United Nations secretaries and told our scientists how much time they were allowed to speak, according to the latest decisions. Many of the scientists prepared in Geneva oral presentations, which were in essence summaries of their papers. The United Nations later published both the papers and the oral versions in the proceedings of the conference.

Most delegates liked to compare notes about their present and past labors and, when asked to tell their stories, they complied readily.

John P. Howe, a quiet metallurgist with a thin narrow face, a lover of both metallurgy and skiing, had prepared a review paper on the metallurgy of fuel elements. Dr. Howe had made fuel elements from the time they were first made; and before that he had helped bring fuel elements about. He had been one of the few metallurgists among the scientists at the Metallurgical Laboratory in Chicago. "Metallurgical Laboratory" was the wartime code name for the project which produced the first pile in 1942. It had been a current joke among its scientists that there were no metallurgists at the Metallurgical Laboratory, although there was much need for them. In response to this need, Dr. Howe had changed, in 1942, from physical chemistry to metallurgy and so became one of the few exceptions. From Chicago he had gone to Hanford where the first large-scale piles for plutonium production were built. He had made fuel elements there and at other places. During the last couple of years he had made fuel elements at North American Aviation, Incorporated, which was constructing reactors in California under contract with the Atomic Energy Commission.

When John Howe and his colleagues had started to discuss the possible contributions of metallurgy to the Geneva conference, they had not spent much time thinking that Howe could present a paper on fuel elements. At that time only fuel elements for research reactors, like the ones built at the Pennsylvania State University, were declassified, and it was not clear which elements of power reactors would be declassified. In this respect John Howe was in a better position than most scientists: he was one of six members of the Committee of Senior Reviewers advising the Commission on classification and declassification matters. So he was able to sort declassifiable material out of the complex and voluminous information accumulated about fuel elements. The description of most fuel elements was declassified before the Geneva conference.

John Howe had only two months to write his paper, and there was no time to gather all the previous reports which he was to review. He wrote the paper out of his memory and checked the references afterward. He worked weekends, evenings, and daytime hours that he took from his regular work. Fortunately, he had not prepared his oral presentation before going to Geneva and so was able to do it there according to the latest instructions.

In this respect Professor Baird Hastings was not so lucky. A white-haired man with a youthful twinkle in his blue eyes, he was the chairman of the department of biochemistry at the Harvard School of Medicine in Boston. When a man has administrative duties, and teaches, and works with students in whom he takes a personal interest, and, being an authority in his field, has to sit on many committees—all of which Professor Hastings did—any extra task like a paper for Geneva requires considerable effort. Professor Hastings had prepared an abstract on the use of isotopes in biochemical and medical research. He managed to write the paper despite an illness that made matters worse. He managed also to prepare the oral presentation of his paper, which, he was told, was to take thirty minutes. In Geneva he learned that his presentation was to be "hacked down" to fifteen minutes; so he had to condense and rewrite it. Finally, he was asked to deliver a medical paper also, the author of which had not come to Geneva. In telling his story, Professor Hastings did not mean to complain, for he was too sympathetic a person not to realize the enormous tasks of those who prepared the program; he was only trying to give an idea of the amount of work behind each paper.

Dr. David Gurinsky of the Brookhaven National Laboratory had had different troubles. He was a young, small man, with red hair and a quiet, unassuming appearance. Looking at him one would hardly have guessed the amount of enthusiasm for his work that was in him. When, slowly, almost uncertainly, as if searching for words, he started talking about reactor fuel, a dull subject for laymen, his listeners doubted they could ever become interested. As he proceeded, his sentences gathered momentum; he became convincing; there was such intensity in his exposition that he seemed the priest of a mystical religion, to which his listeners could not but become converts. He had so much to tell about the fabrication of the fuel elements of the Brookhaven reactor that, when Dr. McDaniel's office asked him to prepare a paper on it, he wrote thirty pages instead of the twelve suggested in the sheet of instructions. His paper was not accepted for oral presentation, but its full text was to be printed in the proceedings of the conference—perhaps just as good a way to spread the word about his religion.

Dr. Vance Sailor, a tall, blond physicist with a serious expression, had another story to tell: he worked at the Brookhaven National Laboratory and when ideas were being collected and co-ordinated at that laboratory for its participation in the conference, Dr. Sailor and his group had suggested five titles for abstracts in the field of uranium cross-sections; in the end, his was the task of writing a review paper covering the five subjects. It was difficult to collect and sift data from the other scientists, and for a month he had worked nights, Saturdays, and Sundays. He had been a bit disappointed in the topic at first, because it did not cover the area in which he felt he had done the best work; but while writing the paper he had become more and more interested in its subject, in fact quite fascinated. Only in Geneva, after receiving the United Nations' instructions, had he become aware that he was to *write* a *verbatim* copy to read from, and that the rate of this reading was predetermined by strict specifications. He then realized that in Geneva he would have very little free time, not only during the conference, which he wanted to attend assiduously, but also in the few days left before it. He was worried lest his wife be bored with nothing to do in Geneva; the trips she might have liked to take in the little Citroën car they had bought for their stay in Europe would have to wait until after the conference. So he advised her to find some occupation; she volunteered her services to the technical delegation and for over two weeks helped to collect historical information.

Two delegates looked very happy in Geneva: Dr. William L. Russell, principal geneticist at the Oak Ridge National Laboratory, and his wife, Dr. Liane B. Russell, a biologist and the only American woman scientist at the conference. Both the Russells were to deliver papers, but until the end of July Mrs. Russell had not known whether she would go to Geneva. In order to limit the size of our delegation, the OIC had established the rule that, if the author of a paper to be delivered orally was also the co-author of another paper, he would deliver both. Dr. William Russell had written a paper on the "Genetic Effects of Radiation in Mice and Their Bearings on the Estimation of Human Hazards"; Dr. Liane Russell's paper on the "Hazards to the Embryo and Fetus from Ionizing Radiation" had also been selected for oral presentation; but, because her husband was co-author of her paper, he had been invited to present both. Only after the middle of July did the OIC decide to name ten or fifteen more delegates, and Mrs. Russell was one of them. Both the Russells had done their research on a colony of about a hundred thousand mice, which they raised at the Oak Ridge National Laboratory. There, room after room, row after row in each room, was filled with neat cages each occupied by a family of mice. Mrs. Russell exposed mother-to-be mice to radiation and studied the malformations in their children. Dr. William Russell was more interested in father mice and in what happened to their progeny during several generations if they had been submitted to radiation.

Some of the delegates had viewed the conference with favor since the moment they had heard about it, but many had at first considered it "just another meeting" and had resolved not to take time from their work to go to Geneva. Sooner or later they had all become enthusiastic about the conference and placed great hopes in it. The outstanding single reason for this change of mind was the large amount of information to be disclosed for the first time at Geneva; this amount was the measure by which they judged the importance of the conference and the willingness of the United States and of other countries advanced in atomic science to share their knowledge with others. The idea that they would be able to talk freely of their work with specialists in the same fields from other countries excited them. It was this excitement, which increased later as the expecta- tions became reality, that accounted in large part for the success of the conference.

Meanwhile our delegates' optimism was necessarily tempered by one uncertainty: how would the Russians behave? It was known by then that Viktor Vavilov, the Deputy Secretary-General of the con- ference, was an extremely co-operative and likable person, and that the same could be said of the other two Russian scientists serving on Professor Whitman's staff of scientific secretaries. But, as a group, would the Russians be friendly? Would they be free to answer quesitons? Would it be possible to establish human contacts with them despite the language barrier?

Our delegates' favorite meeting place for talking about their work, for expressing their hopes and doubts, was the terrace of the Hôtel du Rhône, where they could sit in the sunshine at colored tables, under colored umbrellas, and sip coffee at leisure, in the European fashion. Across the street there was a brief stretch of small wooden stores, in one of which during the Big Four conference, President Eisenhower had walked unescorted to buy toys for his grandchildren, drawing at once a large crowd. This story was still being told in Geneva, along with stories of how Bulganin and Khrushchev had gone around in open cars for all to see them. Look- ing down the street from the terrace, past the main entrance of the hotel, one could see another door with the sign "Entrée—Confé- rences," by which the suitcases bearing our delegation's red, white, and blue tag, were piling up. As the delegates arrived in Geneva, they went straight to the Hôtel du Rhône; at the housing unit's desk in the lobby they were told where rooms had been reserved for them. The housing unit had managed to find accommodations for all, but not necessarily within the city. Some were in neighboring Swiss villages as far away as Lausanne, an hour by train, or across the border in expensive French towns.

Geneva has always been crowded in the summer. The city, which spreads around the western tip of the Lake of Geneva, is situated in an intensely touristic zone at the foot of the highest part of the Alps, dominated by the hazy peaks of Mont Blanc. The city attracts tourists with the placid beauty of its shores and the green, cultivated hills behind them; with the idealistic appeal of international events enhanced by the advent of the League of Nations; with the historical tradition of religious struggles and with the monuments that recalled them. On the summit of the small hill on which spreads the "old city" stands a stately Protestant cathedral in Gothic style; narrow streets cutting between the quaint old buildings climb rapidly and straight toward it. A richly decorated Catholic basilica is in the more modern part of town, near the railroad station.

To accommodate the tourists and the guests of the League of Nations, modern hotels were built; and, as the international gatherings became more frequent, the delegations from the different countries found it more expedient to go back time after time to the same hotels: the British to the Beau Rivage, the French to the Richemond, the Russians to the Metropole, the Americans to the Hôtel du Rhône.

The Hôtel du Rhône was built on the bank of the River Rhône, at a short distance from the place where the river flows out of the lake. The river flows rapidly. At night its rumbling kept awake the most sensitive of our delegates. In the daytime the rumbling mounted above the traffic noise to the fifth and sixth floors of the hotel, where in the offices of the Consulate the staff of our delegation was at work, and disturbed it; but the few times when the water works that regulated the river flow stopped it, the strange stillness that enveloped the hotel seemed more audible than the noise had been.

The Palais des Expositions, the same that is called the Exposition Hall in the English-language documents of the conference, was down and across the river from the Hôtel du Rhône. There the trade fair and the popular exhibit of the United States Information Agency were to be inaugurated officially on Sunday, August 7. Some European countries had announced that they would accord a railroad discount to visitors of this, the first commercial "Atoms for Peace" display at the Palais des Expositions. But, as late as the end of July, no activity was yet visible there. Even two days before the scheduled opening it seemed impossible that everything would be ready on time. The huge hall was in a state of great confusion: exhibit parts, models, pieces of equipment, unlettered posters, were all over; painters, carpenters, workers operating fork-lifts, were moving around with serious deliberation but with no frenzy; buxom, black-aproned women were futilely sweeping away ever re-forming litter from the floor. Unrelated pieces of decoration—metal arcs, flags, colored balls, even a large statue of an atomic worker—were being set up, each to attract attention to a particular country or to a commercial exhibitor.

In the midst of this confusion, Mr. E. F. Crofut, in charge of setting up the exhibit of the United States Information Agency, was perfectly cool and self-possessed. He was so sure that he would have everything ready that he took time to explain his display to people who had come into the hall without meeting anyone to stop them. The visitor, he said, would walk through an introductory aisle—at that moment the most striking piece in the aisle was a huge picture of Einstein's head, two or three times life-size, with the famous formula for the transformation of matter into energy above it, waiting to be hung on a wall—and into a room where he would see the movie "A Is for Atom," which "explained" nuclear science in twelve minutes, from the structure of the nucleus to the production of energy in a reactor. After being so instructed, the visitor would be admitted into the main part of the exhibit, which was dominated by a full-scale, thirty-eight-foot high model of an air-cooled, graphite-moderated reactor, like those at the Brookhaven and the Oak Ridge National Laboratories. A scientist with a Ph.D. would explain its performance, Mr. Crofut said. Although proud of having a Ph.D. at hand, Mr. Crofut was even prouder of having hired pretty science students to act as guides. Professional guides were in general not so pretty as the prettiest students, and therefore not so satisfactory.

The Palais des Nations, built for the League of Nations, is situated a couple of miles from the center of Geneva, to the north, in Ariana Park, which slopes down toward the lake. The Palais is a beautiful building which cuts a long white line in the green hill and rises in majestic splendor from perfectly kept grounds, among beds of salvias and begonias. Shaped in U's and L's, it winds about forward and backward, extending seemingly for miles. Inside, the marble corridors tax the physical endurance of the visitor and their intricate pattern his perspicacity. Some of the corridors end unexpectedly, and to walk from one wing to the other the visitor must go up to a higher floor or down to a lower. Even Mr. Dag Hammarskjöld, the Secretary-General of the United Nations, is said to have lost his way more than once in the maze of corridors, of stairways, of meeting rooms and offices. After the opening of the conference an excellent system of signs and arrows directed the delegates: they may have become tired then, but not lost. Meanwhile the uncautious visitor who went unaccompanied had reason to feel sorry for himself.

On the fifth floor of the Assembly wing of the Palais, Professor Whitman and his staff of scientific secretaries went to work as soon as they arrived from New York. A young Italian physician, Carlo Polvani, had joined their team, which had temporarily lost one of its members: Dr. Charpie had remained in the United States for a very good reason, the arrival of a little daughter, his second child, on August 9. She was welcomed in style by many Geneva-to-Oak-Ridge telegrams, among which were those from Admiral Strauss, Professor Whitman, and the scientific secretaries.

The scientific secretaries were working two by two inside tiny offices filled with tall stacks of paper; they made the final adjustments to the program, adding the last papers that kept flowing in until the fifth of August; they revised the list of delegates as some nations added or changed delegates and as a few late nations sent in their acceptance: the official figure of participating nations rose rapidly from sixty-four to seventy-two just before the conference, and another was added during it. The scientific secretaries helped the interpreters and verbatim reporters to master the jargon of atomic science in English, French, Russian, and Spanish. Interpreters and verbatim reporters, who are said to become the greatest experts in any of the diversified subjects taken up by the United Nations, had attended special science courses for several months. At rehearsal meetings they were asked questions in the most abstruse language that the scientific secretaries, playing the role of delegates, could think up.

The scientific secretaries participated also in a grand rehearsal in the Assembly Hall, when the system for projecting slides was tested. After several difficulties had been encountered and smoothed out, it was discovered that the hall had some forty electric light switches, and that a swiftly running usher took some four minutes to turn them all off. A master switch had to be installed. Similar unexpected problems were likely to arise, and did, in almost all phases of last-minute preparations. Together with the regular staff of the United Nations, the scientific secretaries checked all the cogs of the invisible machinery that was to make the conference run smoothly from its beginning to its successful conclusion.

On the lower floors of the Palais des Nations the pounding of the hammers, the crates being wrenched open in halls and in the garden, the busy workers going in and out, revealed the activities for setting up the technical exhibits. A large model of a British reactor stood sadly at the bottom of a too narrow ramp of stairs. Later it was hoisted up the stair well and reached the British exhibit hall in time for the opening. Workers at each country's exhibits peeked discreetly through doors left ajar into other countries' exhibits, to compare methods and progress.

At the beginning of August the Advisory Committee held its final meeting. It reviewed the preparations, the program, the list of chairmen and vice-chairmen; it made decisions wherever decisions were needed, as in the important matter of how to seat delegations at the general sessions; and it agreed that no more papers would be accepted for the conference after August 5. "The Committee," said Mr. Urquhart in his report, "finally disbanded, leaving Professor Whitman and his staff to complete the final arrangements for the conference."

During the days preceding the opening of the conference a wave of apprehension seemed to spread among the organizers, as if they were suddenly doubting the successful outcome of the conference in which they had so far professed faith and for which they had worked with dedication. Professor Whitman, showing no signs of worry, went about his task apparently calm and unruffled. Yet he revealed his concern when he talked of the difficulties still to be surmounted. He expounded them quietly and objectively, but intensely, as if he were trying to project them on an invisible screen in front of his eyes to scrutinize and evaluate them. How could the problem of transportation be solved? he mused, more to himself than to his listeners. How would three or four thousand people go back and forth between the city and the Palais des Nations? Would they have time to return to the city for lunch during the noon interruption, if they preferred better places than the snack bars that would be set up in the Palais des Nations, or than the crowded eighth-floor restaurant in it? Would they have time to see the exhibits and the films? Would copies of the papers be printed and distributed in time, so that delegates would be able to read them before they were delivered, and be prepared for discussion? Was the program too crammed? Would it be possible for the chairman to keep the schedule, or would discussion periods be used up for delivery of papers?

The scientific secretaries who had already accomplished a huge job were worried about the task still ahead. At each of the conference sessions two of them were to be present. They were to compile the journal with the "programme of sessions" for each day and the daily announcements. They had to attend to many more details. And with sessions lasting from nine to twelve o'clock in the morning and from two-thirty to five-thirty in the afternoon; with an informal half-hour meeting before each session, which all officials and speakers of that session were to attend; with press conferences; with five evenings taken up by lectures, when would they find time to be themselves, scientists who wanted to discuss their work with other scientists, foreigners in Geneva who wanted to see at least a little of the countryside, young husbands who wished to spend at least a few hours with their brides?

George Weil's eyes were narrowed; he talked in short, sharp sentences. The deadline was still much on his mind. The preparations for the technical exhibits, delayed by a strike in Antwerp, where the boat carrying the display components had not been unloaded on schedule, seemed to George Weil to proceed slowly, not to make up for lost time. He went often to see the progress in Salle XV and always found bustling activity, but he found also that Mr. Greenspan, in charge of setting up the exhibits, received constant requests from people who wished a preview. With the finality he put in all his decisions, Dr. Weil dictated one rule only to Mr. Greenspan: "If you think visitors will delay work, answer No, no matter how important the persons who ask. If you are sure they will not interfere with your schedule, let them come."

When the brochures illustrating the reactor erected in Geneva arrived, three or four days before the conference opened, and the French translation was criticized, Dr. Weil's concern became acute. There was no time to correct and reprint the translation. "If the translation is so bad that it may affect our reputation, we must not circulate it. If it is passable, we must use it as is," George Weil decided. He grabbed the telephone, saw that every French-speaking person he could think of had a copy of the brochure and that they all read it and gave their opinions. Among those he asked was Professor Kowarski, a French physicist and a member of the nearby European Center for Nuclear Research. Professor Kowarski's opinion prevailed: while not good, the translation was acceptable. It was not withdrawn.

Dr. Paul McDaniel also was a bit nervous. It was not in his nature to bang his fist on tables and raise his voice. Yet, with a bang on the table and in a loud voice he warned the scientific secretaries of the United States delegation of the job ahead of them. "It is a big job," he said, "and whoever is not prepared to work day and night during the conference should speak up at once." They were to attend sessions; they were to write brief reports on sessions for Dr. McDaniel; they were to write long reports for Mr. Norvell Page, in charge of preparing an exhaustive, documentary, technical report of the United States participation in the Geneva conference; they were to alert the United States Information people about important happenings at the session; they were to be courteous to newsmen, answer their questions, explain science to them. Dr. McDaniel knew he was asking much of his scientific secretaries, but what else could he do? He had worked hard, he was working hard, and he had the fate of the conference very much at heart.

From Dr. Weil and from Dr. McDaniel the unavowed apprehension spread to other members of the OIC. It was as if they were trying to read the future and in doing so they were holding their breath.

Then the conference opened and everything was well.

6 ON THE OPENING DAY AND AFTER

The Conference on the Peaceful Uses of Atomic Energy was officially opened on Monday, August 8, at ten-thirty in the morning. The delegates of seventy-three countries gathered in the vast Assembly Hall, one of the largest halls of its kind in the world. The official representatives occupied seats on the main floor, reserved for them, not according to race, degree of advancement in science, or geographical pattern, but following the alphabetical order of their countries' names, as spelled in French on signs in front of the seats: the representatives of the United States (États Unis) sat next to those of Ethiopia: the representatives of Great Britain (Royaume-Uni) next to those of Rumania; the Italians next to the Israeli. The other delegates, one newspaperman for each paper or magazine, and the luckiest of the observers filled the several rows of balconies and booths. The rest of the observers and public information people sat in two overflow rooms, the one for French-speaking, the other for English-speaking persons.

Almost two thousand people were in the Assembly Hall. Perhaps the best known of all the delegates from all countries, the one who inspired the greatest deference, was Professor Niels Bohr from Denmark, the father of all theories on the atom. Many eyes were turned on him that morning; many persons who had recognized him pointed him out to others. To friends who had not seen him for some time he appeared a little heavier, a little more round-shouldered; but his countenance had not changed; his long eyebrows still brushed his cheeks and his face still expressed a peculiar mixture of idealism and objectivity, of depth of thought, and of childlike helplessness; the fact that only he of all the representatives had his wife at his side was a concession to his fame. Many other prominent scientists in the atomic field were in the audience: Hahn and Strassmann from Germany, the discoverers of nuclear fission; Hevesy from Sweden, pioneer worker with tracers and radioisotopes; Amaldi from Italy, who helped investigate the behavior of slow neutrons;

Auger of UNESCO; Bethe and Wigner, well-known theoretical physicists, Lawrence, the inventor of the cyclotron, and many others from the United States. Not all in the audience were scientists; several countries were represented by their ambassadors and ministers, or by other high officials, for this was not only a scientific conference; it was also a conference of governments.

Most of those present were seeing the Assembly Hall for the first time, and many eyes not only scanned the audience in search of the great in science but wandered on the tall mural paintings in the four corners of the hall, trying to interpret their symbolism; they stopped on the ornate heavy bronze doors richly sculptured with human figures, which now and then opened quietly as a clerk or member of the United Nations staff came in; they turned back toward the smaller doors under the balcony through which all delegates had entered; they examined the large bronze statues of a winged man and woman reclining at the foot of the speakers' platform; they lifted to the platform to take in the polished desks of dark walnut and the people behind them.

Four men faced the audience from behind the highest of the desks: Mr. Max Petitpierre, President of the Swiss Confederation; Mr. Dag Hammarskjöld, Secretary-General of the United Nations; Dr. Homi Bhabha, President of the conference; and Professor Walter Whitman, Secretary-General of the conference.

When, after much picture-taking and light-flashing, Dr. Bhabha called the meeting to order, everyone in the audience donned the earphones provided at each seat. The quaint headgear, forgotten once it had been put on, worn by everyone with the same solemn dignity, became the one trait shared by that multitude of differing types, a symbol of uniformity of needs and aims in the disparity of features. The earphones made it possible for the listener to receive the speeches in the official language he knew best: from soundproof booths the translators read their copies, adjusting the pace of their reading to the pace of delivery of the speech.

As is customary at occasions of this sort, speeches were made and messages were read. The messages were sent by the prime ministers of France, India, the Soviet Union, the United Kingdom, and the President of the United States. They conveyed greetings, underlined the importance of the conference, and expressed the hope that it would bring better understanding among men and better economic conditions. President Eisenhower's message, read by Admiral Strauss, reaffirmed his pledge to the General Assembly of the United Nations in 1953, that the United States was determined to help find the ways by which the inventiveness of man should not be dedicated to his death but consecrated to his life.

The three speeches delivered that morning, taken together, formed a frame defining the scope of the conference. Each placed the major emphasis on one of the conference's aspects: Mr. Petitpierre's speech on the moral value; Mr. Hammarskjöld's on the political implications; Bhabha's on the timing in the history of mankind.

Mr. Petitpierre recalled that ten years before, almost to the day, the first atomic bombs had been dropped on Japan and humanity had learned in a brutal way that a new source of energy had been discovered. Powerful voices had been raised, among them that of Einstein, who had appealed for a new way of thinking if the catastrophe of atomic warfare was to be avoided and if humanity was to survive. The call was heard, and the General Assembly had taken the unanimous decision to convene a technical conference on the peaceful uses of atomic energy.

Mr. Petitpierre then recalled the role played by science in the past and said: "You are privileged men. The field of atomic energy, with which you are familiar, is a mystery to most of your fellow beings . . . thus you have a special power and special responsibilities. It is up to you to open new ways for the utilization of atomic energy, to turn it into benefits and wealth which will help eliminate hunger, poverty and disease. . . . You can set an example by teaching governments and peoples that collaboration is possible for a purpose that goes beyond their antagonisms."

Mr. Hammarskjöld, who called the conference a gathering of "master-builders of nuclear science and nuclear engineering," stressed its unique quality. "When in the history of mankind have men of knowledge, representing so many diverse and distant nations, congregated to offer the best of their minds and goodwill in order to promote knowledge and, through knowledge, peace?" Mr. Hammarskjöld than remembered the initiative taken by the President of the United States; and the Americans in the audience were gratified. Many could not have failed to wonder previously whether this initiative had been forgotten, since all official documents considered the United Nations resolution of December 4, 1954, not President Eisenhower's Atoms for Peace proposal, as the starting point of the conference.

Mr. Hammarskjöld, like the other two speakers, examined the role of atomic energy both in its destructive and in its constructive phases; then he evaluated the political significance of the conference. "In its conception, its purposes and its approach," he said, "this conference is as nonpolitical as a conference of this nature should be. The personalities that we see around us are not concerned with expedience, with strategy, with tactics of any kind, but with the search for truth and with the idea of brotherhood based on the concept that all knowledge is universal. Nevertheless, since their deliberations are bound to affect human life in all its aspects, it would not be correct to say that they have no political significance. I am sure that their co-operation will ease tensions. I am sure that their exchange of scientific data will inspire confidence and I am sure that the trend of their discussions will turn men's thoughts away from war to peace. . . ."

Dr. Bhabha's presidential address was, fittingly, the longest of the three speeches. After a few opening words he stated that the history of mankind could be divided into three epochs, each marked by a change in the energy pattern of society. The first epoch was by far the longest: man has existed for well over 250,000 years, though the earliest recorded civilization dates back only 8,000 years. During the first epoch all the energy for doing mechanical work was supplied by muscle, either human or animal. The second epoch was marked by the widespread use of chemical energy, especially that obtained by burning fossil fuels—coal and oil—which led to the industrial revolution and the present pattern of industrialized society.

Since the beginning of the industrial revolution, the total consumption of energy in the world has gone up in a staggering manner, Dr. Bhabha stated. The current rate of consumption is about twenty times what it was during the eighteen and a half centuries after Christ, before the industrial revolution. How the world's demands for energy were to continue to increase in the future, Dr. Bhabha said, was one of the important subjects which the conference would discuss. Many factors entered into an answer to this question: the population of the world is growing rapidly; the per capita utilization of energy has also been going up during the last twenty years; most of the materials needed for industrialization are being fast consumed and soon they may no longer be available; 80 per cent of the world's consumption of energy is currently provided by combustion of fossil fuel—coal and oil; the reserves of fossil fuel were formed by nature during the Carboniferous age, some 250 million years ago, and we have been exhausting them in a few centuries, a flash of geological time.

Bhabha expressed his regret at the fact that large populations were not represented at the conference, so that their views were not under consideration in the discussions about fuel resources and power needs of the world. He then asserted that if the entire world population were to consume energy at the same per capita rate as the United States, and if the increase in population were to be what we expect, the known reserves of fossil fuels would be exhausted in less than a century.

This conclusion proved the absolute necessity of finding some new source of energy. "The acquisition by Man of the knowledge of how to release and use atomic energy must be recognized as the third great epoch in human history," he said. There was no longer any question that atomic energy could be used for power generation, because it had already been used on a small scale. In presenting the economical and technical problems that had been solved and those still to be solved, he outlined the course of the conference. At the same time, by pointing out the fact that it was not possible to separate entirely the "applications of peace from the applications of war," he came to the conclusion that "a widespread atomic power industry in the world will necessitate an international society in which the major states have agreed to maintain peace."

The use of atomic energy released by the fission process might be regarded one day as the primitive period of atomic energy. "It is well known," he explained, "that atomic energy can also be obtained by a fusion process, as in the H-bomb. . . . The technical problems are formidable. . . . I venture to predict that a method will be found for liberating fusion energy in a controlled manner within the next two decades. When that happens, the energy problems of the world will truly have been solved forever, for the fuel will be as plentiful as the heavy hydrogen in the oceans."

Bhabha concluded his speech by remarking that the conference had already broken down many barriers among countries and that all who participated in it had the unique opportunity of giving their knowledge to others for the common good. He expressed the hope that the conference would "play its part in helping the progress of mankind toward the ever-widening dawn of the atomic age, with the promise of a life fuller and happier than anything we can visualize today."

Bhabha, self-assured, speaking with ease in perfect English and clearly enjoying his speech, following with his mobile eyes the reaction of the audience, admirably filled his role of president, both that morning and afterward. He received the long applause at the end of his speech with seeming satisfaction while walking down from the orator's podium and back to his seat.

It was then Mr. Whitman's turn to ask confirmation of the six vice-presidents of the conference: General Bernardino C. de Mattos of Brazil; Dr. W. B. Lewis of Canada; Professor Francis Perrin of France; Professor D. V. Skobeltzin of the Soviet Union; Sir John Cockcroft of Great Britain; and Dr. I. I. Rabi of the United States. They were confirmed by acclamation. Then the meeting adjourned.

The anticipated problem of transportation was well under control both that morning and during the entire time of the conference. Special busses drove the largest delegations back and forth from their hotels to the Palais des Nations; others rounded up those unfortunate delegates who had to stay in villages outside Geneva; public transportation did its part efficiently; and every day countless private cars filled the ample parking spaces on the grounds of the Palais. Taxis, with and without meters, each time charging a different fee for the same distance, shuttled from one end of town to the other between hotels, restaurants, or private villas and the Palais.

The United States delegation, being by far the most numerous, had the most frequent private bus service. At first their schedule was not clear either to the delegates or to the bus drivers. On one of the first days a Swiss driver, asked around one o'clock in the afternoon what time he would depart for town, answered that he would wait until he had about fifteen passengers. After a few minutes, with a broad yawn and a disappointed glance at the only two delegates in the bus, he declared that he was going to leave: "J'ai faim" ("I am hungry"), he explained with the simple finality of the basic needs of life, and drove off. The busses left from the entrance of the Hôtel du Rhône. There was never any uncertainty about this. But for a few days it was not clear whether they left the Palais des Nations from the monumental entrance of the Assembly Hall or from the bottom of the stairs leading to the reactor building or from the entrance door of the library wing containing our exhibits.

Busses and cars discharged their passengers at Porte XIV of the Palais, the pillared entrance to the wing housing the Assembly Hall. On entering, the delegates were asked to show their passes to the Swiss guards despite the blue and white tag marked with name and country which each delegate wore pinned on his lapel. They crowded the lobby, whose vast extent of granite floors was meant to induce purposeless wandering, judging by its name, "Salle des Pas Perdus" or the "Hall of the Lost Steps."

There, before the sessions started, nationalities were mixed at random, colors and features seemed to have been shuffled and tossed about; there each delegate scanned those features in search of known faces; there the first reunions among old friends from distant lands took place; there hopes for the day were expressed in the morning and comments on the day were made later. The lobby emptied suddenly when the sessions started, and then the details of the grandiose structure stood out; the pillars, the luscious marbles, the ample stairways ascending to the upper floors, the tall floodlights.

The general sessions were held in the Assembly Hall; but when, after the first three days, there were always three concurrent sessions, two more rooms were needed. One amazing feature of the Palais des Nations was the number of rooms supplied with wiring and equipment for simultaneous translations. In Salle VII, where the chemistry, metallurgy, and technology sessions were held, each seat was so equipped. Salle XII, the seat of the biological and medical sessions, was not so thoroughly wired; the delegates entering this room picked a portable receiving set, a sort of walkie-talkie, from a coat rack on which scores of them, perhaps a few hundred, were neatly hanging. Salle III was another completely wired and equipped room, with earphones and switches at each seat; there, members of the press listened to the chairmen's reports after the closing of the sessions at noon and at five-thirty in the afternoon; and interesting press conferences were held with top representatives of various countries, at which the questions asked always seemed to pry beyond what the answers were willing to reveal.

Besides permitting selection of the desired language, the earphones had another advantage: it was as if the speaker were talking directly into the listener's ears, and so the mild activities always going on in the lecture rooms did not disturb the audience. Delegates entered or left at all times; engrossed in what they were hearing, they let pads and notebooks drop from their laps; messages were conveyed to chairmen and secretaries. Without earphones the sound of all this would have diverted the attention of many.

Discussion periods caused some difficulties. At the general sessions in the Assembly Hall, if a man got up to ask a question, a clerk on the floor rushed toward him with a microphone. Often, in his eagerness not to delay the discussion, the clerk would run and get entangled in the yards of wire attached to the microphone. Scientific questions asked in the course of discussion periods, for which there were no prepared copies to read from, taxed the translators' abilities to the limit; through the earphones came precipitous flows of words often broken by sighs and brief spells of stammering. Although no better translations could be expected and although discussions proceeded in a lively manner most of the time, there were occasional misunderstandings. It is not known, for instance, by what Russian word a translator rendered the English "practical" when a Russian scientist was asked about certain "practical" details; he answered with some irritation that he was a scientist and knew nothing of costs. When the misunderstanding was cleared up, the Russian scientist expressed the wish that questions be asked him in slow, well-enunciated English, which he was able to understand.

From the lecture halls delegates circulated through the polished marble corridors to the snack bars, to the exhibits, to places where they could sit in twos or threes and talk. No matter where they were going, they could hardly avoid walking through the Canadian technical exhibit on the gallery in front of the Assembly Hall. When an attempt was made to compare the attendance at the various scientific exhibits, it became apparent that attendance at the Canadian exhibit could not be evaluated. Each delegate had gone through it dozens of times, if for nothing else than to stop at one of the two snack bars in front of it.

While sipping coffee and eating brioches, they could not avoid the view of the Canadians' prize exhibit, a cobalt teletherapy machine called Theratron, demonstrating its use in hospitals: it was turned down as if directing its beam on a life-size woman patient lying in a hospital bed. The very real-looking woman under white sheets was somewhat of a shock at first to coffee drinkers, but quite soon they became used to her, and the snack bars never lacked customers. The girls behind the bars spoke only French, yet in one way or another all the delegates managed to get what they wanted—or at least something.

These two snack bars were for "standing only," but a third one was set up in Salle VI, a committee room frescoed by a Swiss painter, where one large conference table and several small ones were turned into luncheon tables. Delegates crowded Salle VI at lunch time when they did not want to wait for the slower meals served in the restaurants. Swiss girls behind the bar dished out large quantities of plain food from huge pots into too small dishes—the most popular menu with people of all races was potato salad and sausages.

Salle VI, which was best known for its bar, was also the seat of many unofficial activities. Representatives of British industries discussed reactor sales with people from underdeveloped countries and thus created the impression that England was ready to sell reactors; but Sir John Cockcroft and Sir Christopher Hinton declared that not for another year would England be ready even to quote prices and that the first reactors might at best be sold in 1960. The members of the Pakistani delegation met in the bar twice a day, after the sessions, presumably to confer on the value of the information just acquired. Scientists who had promised to write articles on the Geneva conference sat dejectedly in the bar, reflecting on the rashness of their promise. Press people and history-writers buttonholed scientists and members of governments.

Scientists are by tradition mistrustful of reporters, whom they accuse of seeking sensationalism and of distorting truth for the sake of it. Reporters, on the other hand, accuse the scientists of neglecting their duty to inform the public through the press and of not trying to make their language understandable. In Geneva past differences were forgotten. By tacit accord reporters and scientists united to give an exhaustive and objective account of the conference to the public. Taking advantage of the novel mood, reporters interviewed scientists not only in the bar but wherever and whenever they could. Men of science and of the press were seen standing together in the corridors, walking together, or sitting amiably on the benches along the walls; they were seen together in the exhibits or outdoors on the grounds of the Palais. Eminent men like Niels Bohr bent down in earnest talk with young girl reporters who were raptly drinking in each word and scribbling on their pads. And the cameras kept on flashing.

Perhaps the only place in the Palais des Nations where press people did not try to get interviews or pictures was the music room. At Professor Whitman's initiative the French Lounge, near the French exhibits, had been equipped with the best possible high-fidelity equipment. Whitman thought that music, a language needing no translation, might provide mental rest to tired delegates. He had spoken of this idea to Mr. Adrian Pelt, Director of the European Office of the United Nations, who agreed to reserve a room for this purpose. Professor Whitman then had received support for his project from the members of the "Fund for Peaceful Atomic Development, Inc." The fund installed the equipment and furnished three hundred records, a much-appreciated gift to the United Nations.

Walt Whitman often wandered into this music room, of which he was justly proud. He liked to see delegates sunk in the deep, comfortable, wine-colored armchairs, listening to Bach, Brahms, or Bartók. The softness of the luxurious rug and of the drapes hanging on immensely tall windows, the large gilded mirror and the smaller painted ones, the gilded molding on the walls and on the ceiling, together with the excellent music, created an atmosphere of refinement seldom encountered.

If the music room caused the greatest satisfaction to Professor Whitman, he had still other reasons to be pleased. Before the opening of the conference he had not admitted to any real concern. Yet as the conference evolved he conceded that he was increasingly relieved. The fact that everything was proceeding well was evidenced by the delegates' mounting good spirits, he observed. They appeared more and more cheerful, more engrossed in the scientific sessions, busier with informal discussions and with new friendships.

The delivery of papers was proceeding on time, thanks to the chairmen and the scientific secretaries; the three time clocks that the secretaries had procured, one for each session, had rung out their sharp, business-like reminder only on few occasions. Sessions and technical exhibits were well attended, a fact which went to prove that delegates found time for both. There were no complaints except some mild criticism of the fact that for a few days papers were not distributed early enough for delegates to study them and be prepared for discussion. The timing of the distribution had improved, and, in any case, the criticism had not been harsh, since all realized the immensity of the task involved in the preparation of conference documents.

A backlog had built up at the bindery, where by August 7 there were twelve tons of documents, according to Brian Urquhart. He reported that "at one time there were thirteen printing and binding firms engaged simultaneously on the documentation of the conference." At the end of the first week of the conference a Swiss newspaper published an article in a jocular rather than factual vein, in which it estimated that two hundred tons of assorted documents— the great bulk of them scientific papers—had been sorted out and distributed to satisfy that "factory of words, the United Nations." Undoubtedly, the article concluded, large quantities of nuclear energy had transformed into paper!

The United Nations scientific secretaries had lost their tense look; they no longer felt sorry for themselves. They had become interested in the sessions that they attended out of duty and did find time to deliver their own papers and to talk with other scientists. They were usually kept busy in the lecture halls or in their offices, but they were occasionally seen in the corridors talking animatedly on some subject such as the genetic effects of radiation or the corrosion problems in aluminum.

Bhabha's presidential address, an account of which appeared earlier in this chapter, was an excellent and, in appearance, typical opening speech which set the stage for what was to come. Yet it was more than this: it contained two unexpected statements which caused surprise. "It is a matter of regret," he had said, "that there are several areas of the world which are not directly represented at this Conference," and whose populations constitute a quarter of the total world's population. This reference to the exclusively political issue of the admission to the United Nations of Communist China and other countries seemed out of place to many delegates. The conference, they argued, was to be scientific, and political questions had been deliberately banned from it. Some of the scientists expressed concern that this one issue might bring forth others, and that the purely scientific character of the conference might be jeopardized. This apprehension proved unfounded, for Bhabha's remark was not played up.

Another of his statements caused a great sensation. "I venture to predict," he had said, "that a method will be found for liberating fusion energy in a controlled manner within the next two decades."

Fusion was not on the conference agenda. It was not mentioned in any paper. As Bhabha himself pointed out, it was well known that fusion takes place in the explosion of a hydrogen bomb and was therefore believed to be of exclusively military interest.

Fusion and fission are very different. Fission is the splitting of a nucleus of a heavy element, like uranium or plutonium, into two lighter nuclei, with release of energy. Fusion reactions are those that occur between very light nuclei, like the isotopes of hydrogen, which combine to form heavier nuclei, also with release of energy. Fission is caused by neutrons, which have no electrical charge and can easily approach and enter nuclei; neutrons produce fission best if they have been slowed down and have kinetic energies corresponding to ordinary temperatures; thus fission can take place at room temperatures.

In the case of fusion, two nuclei must come close together and combine. But all nuclei are positively charged and repel each other; they show no natural inclination to approach one another and fuse. To make them overcome the electrostatic repulsion, they must be heated to extremely high temperatures, comparable to those existing in the interior of the sun and of large stars. At these temperatures their velocity is sufficient to make them collide and undergo fusion reactions. Because fusion reactions take place at temperatures of millions of degrees, they are also called thermonuclear reactions. Fission gives origin to fission products many of which are highly radioactive. In fusion, neutrons or protons may be freed, but no radioactivity is created.

The fusion process is a much older object of theoretical study and of scientific speculation than fission. As far back as 1920 the British astrophysicist Arthur Eddington suggested that the energy of the sun and of the other large stars might be due to fusion of hydrogen into helium. In 1939 Hans Bethe, one of the most prominent United States delegates to the conference, developed a theory of nuclear fusion reactions, in agreement with the rate of energy liberation from the sun. It is generally accepted that all the light and heat emitted by the sun are due to fusion reactions transforming hydrogen into helium in its interior, where the temperature is a few hundred million degrees.

When the explosion of a thermonuclear device was announced in the United States, it was generally assumed that the required temperatures were achieved by detonating an atomic bomb. Since the high temperature of the fission bomb lasts only an exceedingly tiny fraction of a second, it was regarded as useful only to trigger an explosion. The non-specialists came to the conclusion that the only possible manner of achieving fusion reactions on earth was by an explosion, and that it would be impossible to contain the explosion because at those extremely high temperatures any container would vaporize.

Thus Bhabha caused much understandable surprise when in his presidential address he stated that "there is no basic scientific knowledge in our possession today to show that it is impossible for us to obtain this energy from the fusion process in a controlled manner." Bhabha implied that the nuclear fuel to be used in controlled fusion was heavy hydrogen, also called deuterium, an isotope of twice the atomic weight of common hydrogen. Deuterium is contained in all waters, including those of the oceans, in the proportion of one part to about six thousand, and, if all of it were extracted and made to fuse, the power requirements of the world could be filled for millions of years.

As soon as the opening session was over, startled newspapermen ran after delegates to obtain more information. In their first articles describing the opening of the conference they reported that United States scientists had refused to comment on fusion but that the British had admitted that some work on controlled thermonuclear reactions was under way in their country.

The newspapermen did not give up. On the afternoon of the opening day Admiral Strauss held a previously scheduled press conference. He had a couple of announcements to make (of which more will be said in later chapters), and these announcements led to questioning by the reporters. After this, one of the press people managed to broach the subject of fusion. It was late. The afternoon session was about to begin, as indicated by the buzzing of Admiral Strauss's wrist alarm clock, which he invariably wore and which contributed to his efficiency. So Strauss agreed to take the matter up in a couple of days.

Meanwhile another group of people had become much interested in fusion, had expressed concern, and were asking for information: the businessmen. Business was on the point of investing enormous amounts of capital in the future atomic industry, in reactors and atomic power plants. Business was already placing capital in uranium mines. It had sent its representatives to the Geneva conference to learn all there was to learn about atomic technology so that the new industry and the new economy could be based on the soundest foundations. It had sent representatives to investigate the prospects of selling reactors to other countries, once these countries would be sufficiently trained in atomic science to use them safely. Atomic industry had seemed a long-range but sound program. And now Bhabha had calmly speculated that "the historical period . . . in which . . . fission process will supply some of the power . . . may well be regarded as the primitive period of the atomic age." Did he mean, the businessmen wanted to know, that the technology presented at Geneva might become suddenly obsolete, that all the efforts put into creating the new industry would be futile, that investments in this industry would become worthless?

Only the scientists seemed unaffected by Bhabha's revelation.

Perhaps fusion had been known so long to them that those interested in speculating about it had already done so. Bhabha's speech gave no specific information that might modify previous thinking. Be that as it may, talk of fusion was not heard among scientists in Geneva unless non-scientists asked questions on the subject.

On August 10, two days after Bhabha's address, Sir John Cockcroft and Sir Edwin Plowden, Chairman of the United Kingdom Atomic Energy Authority, held a press conference in which they admitted that Britain was investigating the controlled fusion reaction, and they spoke of fusion power "within a generation."

On August 11, at the press conference Chairman Strauss had promised, he disclosed that the Atomic Energy Commission had been working for a considerable time on a program directed at the study of controlled thermonuclear reactions. He called it a "moderate" program and stated that there had been progress, which sometimes consisted only of finding that things could not be done. The program, he said, was of such long range that it would not affect the future of uranium as fuel for reactors. Despite the numerous questions asked, Mr. Strauss refused to make further comments at that time on the United States fusion program, but professed himself willing to take up the matter again in the fall, in Washington.

The following day it was Bhabha's much-deserved turn to be under fire of questions from the press. He stood it as well as Chairman Strauss. Showing no sign of compunction for the fuss he had caused, he seemed to enjoy the performance. He answered questions readily; yet by the end of the conference he had not disclosed much information. Perhaps, he said, it will be possible to ignite a fusion reaction by other means than an atomic bomb, and high-current accelerators might provide a way; perhaps fusion may take place at lower temperatures than those produced by the explosion of a fission bomb and existing in the stars. Even if accelerators capable of producing the necessary temperatures were built, he said, the problem of controlling the fusion reaction would still have to be solved. He thought there would always be a place for fission reactors even in a world where power from fusion was available. In India, he said, there was no fusion program except a few theoretical calculations. He repeated that the harnessing of the fusion reaction might well come within the next two decades. The line of reasoning he followed in making his prediction was that less than fifteen years had passed since Fermi had first released atomic energy, and already atomic power from fission was assured. The first hydrogen "device" had been exploded in 1952; so why not expect power from fusion within some fifteen or twenty years?

Some scientists raised objections to this argument. They pointed out that the cases of fission and of fusion were different. Fission energy was released for the first time in a controlled way in the Chicago pile. In learning how to make uranium yield energy through fission, scientists had also learned how to build a reactor. The bomb, the flash release of nuclear energy from fission, had come only at a later time. Fusion, on the other hand, had so far been achieved on earth only in an explosion, and one of the main problems of controlling fusion consisted in finding ways to avoid the explosion.

Sir John Cockcroft made a few more remarks on fusion in the course of a lecture delivered on Friday, August 19, the day before the closing of the conference. His speech was one of the most interesting of the ten evening lectures. In it he summarized the material presented at the conference in his characteristically lively and objective way. Toward the end he said: "Having looked into the cloudy crystal ball with my imperfect eyes I feel quite sure that the real picture 25 years hence will be quite different. . . . I would like tonight to have been able to predict when the exciting prospect of power from fusion reactions would be achieved. But although we are working seriously on this problem in Britain, my vision is not good enough for that. I am not as bold as Dr. Bhabha, our president. I am sure that he would not mind my saying that the experimental physicist must inevitably have a greater appreciation of the problems and difficulties than the theoretical physicist. However, my faith in the creative ability of the scientists is so great that I am sure that this will be achieved long before it is essential for man's needs."

Here matters rested when the conference closed in Geneva. True to his word, Chairman Strauss held a press conference to discuss controlled fusion on October 3 in Washington. On that day he announced that the Atomic Energy Commission was carrying on its major research effort in controlled thermonuclear reactions at Princeton University and at Atomic Energy Commission laboratories at Los Alamos, New Mexico, and at Livermore, California. In addition, there were projects at Oak Ridge, Tennessee, and at New York University. The over-all research program was given the code name "Project Sherwood"; the program at Princeton was called "Project Matterhorn," from the name of the mountain whose peak remained unattained for many years although men had often tried to reach it.

At this press conference Admiral Strauss stated that some time before the Geneva conference the Atomic Energy Commission had decided to announce its interest in the controlled thermonuclear reaction at the conference but that Dr. Bhabha had taken the initiative with his opening speech. From Mr. Strauss's statement and from other announcements made simultaneously at each site where research was being carried on, the state of the problem can be summarized as follows. Study of the controlled thermonuclear reaction had been undertaken as early as 1951, when Professor Lyman Spitzer of Princeton University approached the Atomic Energy Commission with an idea for containing and controlling fusion reactions at temperatures comparable to those of the sun. Professor Spitzer had directed the research at Princeton from the start.

Fusion of light nuclei, or thermonuclear burning, occurs most readily with deuterium, the heavy isotope of hydrogen. It occurs only at enormously high temperatures, above one hundred million degrees Fahrenheit, which have existed so far only at the center of hot stars or during the explosion of an atomic bomb. To convert the inexhaustible supply of energy in the earth's deuterium into useful power, those temperatures must be achieved in a gas confined within walls that remain relatively cool. The thermonuclear reaction must be controlled when it occurs. The energy released must be extracted and used to generate electricity. The scientific and technical difficulties to be surmounted are formidable. Chairman Strauss said also: "It cannot be stressed too strongly that, based on what we now know, we are far from a solution of the problems of the controlled fusion reactions."

7 A REACTOR FLIES EAST

On a hill that sloped down toward the library wing of the Palais des Nations, among cedars and chestnut trees, poplars and cypresses, there was, during the conference, a small wooden chalet with modern lines that bore the United States emblem of the Atoms for Peace. It housed the research reactor flown from Oak Ridge, Tennessee, in what came to be known as "Project Aquarium." This name was due to the pool in which the reactor core was immersed, a deep cylinder filled with water so clear that it would be the envy of any aquarium builder.

The visitor entering the building through its main door would not notice the pool at first, for only the top part of the reactor stood out above the floor: the neat assembly of polished aluminum rods and bars, the two large instruments continuously recording the reactor performance and the square frame that bound them, the railing around the circular brim of the pool. At this sight the visitor would wonder that such a beautiful thing, so perfectly designed to please the eye, was not a museum piece but a tool of research. Then, advancing over the soft, dark linoleum floor, he would reach the rail and see the pool, twenty feet deep and ten in diameter, the level of the water just above the floor, and at the bottom, far away but perfectly clear through the amazing transparency of the filtered water, the fuel elements and the thin control rods that entered into them stretching all the way from the top.

If the visitor had leaned over the railing of the pool and had accidentally dropped a small object, perhaps a pen or a pencil from his pocket, he would have thought it floated: one inch or so below the water level there was a plastic lid, but so transparent that it went unnoticed.

When a light was turned on under the water, the whole structure became softly illuminated in greenish aqueous tones; but when the reactor was in operation and its power had reached at least ten kilowatts, all lights were turned out and an intense blue glow appeared around the fuel elements, the Cerenkov radiation; at the same time two bright spots appeared, one green, the other orange, like two small windows in the bottom of the tank: a piece of willmenite and a piece of tremolite inclosed in an invisible lucite box had become intensely fluorescent. As the core developed heat and transmitted it to the water, currents were formed and tiny ripples stirred the surface of the pool.

Having delighted in the sight of the reactor at the center of the building, the visitor, turning around, would see to the right of the front wall a large glass partition and behind it the instrument panel from which the reactor was started and its performance controlled. Then he would notice the exhibit panels displayed along the walls: an actual fuel element, a control rod and the electromagnet that could raise it; the simulator which reproduced by electronic devices the action of the reactor, even to producing the blue glow; and the showcases illustrating various experiments that could be performed with the reactor and various uses of it. All explanations and captions in the building were in the four official languages: English, French, Russian, and Spanish.

The idea of exhibiting a real reactor in Geneva was conceived in Oak Ridge in the late fall of 1954. The United Nations had not yet called the conference, but it seemed likely that they would, and for some time the scientists of the Oak Ridge National Laboratory had been discussing the contributions that they could make to the success of the international gathering.

One night, in one of the town's many identical homes, a young physicist, Tom Cole, woke up his blue-eyed wife to ask her opinion about a thought that had just occurred to him. Many foreign scientists visiting Oak Ridge, he said, had professed skepticism about the possibility of doing anything conclusive with the fissionable material that President Eisenhower had offered to lease to foreign countries. Well, why not build a reactor with that fuel and send it to Geneva to demonstrate the meaning and the possibilities of Eisenhower's proposal? The wife had worries of her own; her blue eyes were misty and sleepy. There is no record whether she gave her husband the encouragement he was seeking.

All the same, the idea of the Geneva reactor emerged from the physicist's home, perhaps vague, shy, with no confidence in its chances of being accepted; but at once it found an enthusiastic supporter in Robert Charpie, the physicist whom Professor Rabi had placed in charge of pooling suggestions for the Geneva conference. The idea not only pleased Bob Charpie; it set on fire his easily aroused imagination. So backed now by a vigorous, self-confident, promoter, the idea of exhibiting a reactor started on a long trip, first to the luncheon tables and conference halls in Oak Ridge, then all the way to Washington and into the Atomic Energy Commission building. Everywhere it received the same reception: "It would be wonderful to show a real reactor in Geneva. But it cannot be done; it would take three years at least." "We can do it," replied the men from Oak Ridge; "we will."

The official sanction for a reactor came at the beginning of March, after our government had received the United Nations invitation to the conference and had set up an office under Dr. George Weil's direction to organize our participation; but some unofficial activity had already gone on during the preceding months. At Oak Ridge the reactor physicists and engineers had consulted with the officials of Union Carbide and Carbon Corporation, which operated the Oak Ridge National Laboratory for the Atomic Energy Commission.

Two facts were immediately apparent: first, that both the researchers and the administrative personnel, being enthusiastic about the project, were willing to work extra hours and make available all facilities at their disposal. Second, that if the conference were to take place in August, as seemed most probable, the time would be extremely tight and the reactor would have to be shipped by air. To send it all assembled, in one piece, was out of the question. After the necessary tests in Oak Ridge and a suitable "cooling" period to let the radioactivity die down, it would have to be disassembled and its parts crated separately. Still some of the components would be large, and, once crated, even larger. The greatest dilemma was caused by the control panel: it could be built in separate parts, but then the electronics would become very complicated, and it would take so long to assemble the parts that the August date could not be met. If, on the other hand, the panel were made in one piece, the deadline could be met but the crated panel would be so large that it was doubtful whether a plane could fly it. The Military Air Transport System, unofficially consulted, said they could manage it.

In February, as plans were taking shape, some tentative orders went out for parts, but not until early March, after Project Aquarium had received official sanction, did the real activity start. Most of the men at Oak Ridge could not leave the work they were already doing during the day and so they devoted night hours to the reactor—from seven in the evening to as late as two in the morning. This schedule was particularly efficient, Tom Cole explained later in the quiet tone of the researcher not impressed by his own achievements, because they could figure out their requirements one night, place orders accordingly to the shop the next morning on their way to their regular business, and have the necessary equipment ready by the evening, when they returned to the reactor project.

A reactor of the type now planned was already in operation at Oak Ridge; the water in which its core was immersed served several purposes: it acted as a coolant, dispersing the heat produced by the chain reaction; as a moderator, slowing the neutrons to a speed at which they would be most efficient to produce fission and the chain reaction; as a reflector, to return to the reactor some of the neutrons that tried to escape; and as a protective shielding to absorb radiations. Besides, it permitted complete visibility of the reactor core and of experiments in progress. The tank containing the water, large and rectangular in shape, gave origin to the colloquial expression "swimming pool reactor." This expression was sometimes inappropriately used also to denote the Geneva reactor, whose pool was small and circular, and it created understandable confusion. One day during the conference a woman with a swimming suit on her arm asked the girls at the exhibit desk where the swimming pool was that the Americans had installed in the gardens of the Palais des Nations.

It would seem that the physicists and the engineers planning the Geneva reactor had only to copy the one in Oak Ridge, making minor modifications, as in the size, which was to be as small as possible, and in the appearance, which was to be neat and appealing to the eye. But matters were not this simple; a problem arose at once. The fuel material made available to foreign countries by President

Eisenhower was enriched uranium, containing 20 per cent of uranium 235. The Geneva reactor ought to utilize this same type of fuel, if it was to serve as a demonstration to other countries; but fuel of this composition had never been used in the United States, and it was not known how best to fabricate it into practical fuel elements.

Theoretical considerations and results of previous experimental work indicated that the fuel elements should consist of sandwiches of thin aluminum cladding filled with a mixture of powdered aluminum and uranium oxide. So the scientists set to work. The sandwiches had to be extremely thin and could not be prepared like regular sandwiches, by cutting slices and spreading them with the filling. Instead, the filling first had to be prepared by mixing thoroughly the uranium oxide and aluminum powder, like any batter, and then by submitting the mixture to a pressure of thirty tons per square inch. This mixture had then to be used to fill little sandwiches measuring two by two and a half inches, and each little sandwich had to be rolled out to become three inches wide and twenty-four inches long; its thickness was thus reduced to one-sixteenth of an inch, the thickness of fifteen sheets or so of common writing paper. Eighteen parallel sandwiches brazed at regular distances from one another into a pair of aluminum spacer plates were to form a fuel element.

Some of the early elements were a failure; the heat from the brazing process made the sandwiches blister and warp: the aluminum reduced the uranium oxide, with consequent formation of gas. Under normal conditions it would take at least a year of patient study to overcome a difficulty of this kind. It took six weeks. The method of preparing the uranium oxide was changed; a different size of particles was selected; the brazing process was modified. Then seventy-two hours of work around the clock produced successful sandwiches.

Next, the sandwiches were curved slightly lengthwise like rain gutters under the eaves of a roof. This shape had been devised by a scientist while designing the elements for another reactor. His sandwiches were to be spaced to allow water to circulate between them and to remove the heat produced by fission. But the sandwiches were so thin and long that they might easily warp; if they warped in different directions, it might happen that two sandwiches would come in contact, preventing the circulation of water and excessive heat at the point of contact. "How can the sandwiches be instructed to warp all in the same direction?" the scientist had asked himself. Suddenly the idea of curving them had occurred to him: any warping would then necessarily follow the direction of the curve.

March, April, and May were spent solving these problems and others and in building and assembling the various components, until on June 3, right after supper, the new reactor was ready to be tested. It was the guest of honor in the swimming pool: the regular inhabitant, the Oak Ridge reactor, which could move back and forth along the middle line of the pool, had retired to the far end. Its hospitality did not stop there: it lent its fuel elements to the Geneva reactor for the night. If the Geneva elements had been used in a test at full power, they would have become intensely radioactive, thus adding to the difficulties of the shipping: radioactive material can travel only if inclosed in lead boxes, which greatly increase its weight.

During the test, which lasted until three in the morning, all the men held their breath. What machine as delicate as this does not need some adjustment when first tested? And what adjustment does not require many days of patient work? But the Geneva reactor worked perfectly with the borrowed elements, and not only once. It was brought to its full power of one hundred kilowatts, then stopped and started again many times. A well-deserved miracle!

Later the fuel elements, which had proved entirely satisfactory when tested in another reactor weeks before, were placed in the Geneva reactor and the entire assembly was tested at low power, to avoid building up excessive radioactivity.

The Geneva reactor had a special feature: it was fully automatic and could be started and brought to full power by pressing just one button. Its core consisted of twenty-three fuel elements compactly arranged and mounted on an aluminum grid plate supported from the bottom of the tank. The active core was composed of 18 kilograms of uranium of which 20 per cent, or 3.6 kilograms, was fissionable uranium 235. Three of the fuel elements contained holes in which three control rods of boron carbide were inserted. When the starting button was pushed, each of three electromagnets would slowly pull a control rod out of its hole and a chain reaction would take place. Its intensity could be regulated by adjusting the position of the rods. Then in the water that surrounded the core the blue glow would appear.

This glow is called the Cerenkov radiation because it was discovered by the Russian scientist Cerenkov in 1934, while he was preparing a thesis on luminescence under the guidance of Professor Vavilov, the father of Viktor Vavilov, Deputy Secretary-General of the Geneva conference. Cerenkov observed that, when he irradiated a flask of water with gamma rays from radium, the water would emit a bluish light. Three years later two Russian theoretical physicists, Tamm and Frank, proved that the Cerenkov radiation is produced every time fast particles travel in a certain medium at a velocity greater than that of light in the same medium. In the case of the pool reactor, the gamma rays produced during the fission process hit the electrons in the water imparting to them sufficient energy to produce the Cerenkov radiation.

Like radiations, rumors seem to originate from nothing; like radiations, they spread fast. Before the conference, a rumor spread that Cerenkov himself would be at Geneva. The workers at Oak Ridge looked forward to meeting him; they yearned for the day when he would come to see the reactor in its Geneva home, and they could tell him: "You discovered this radiation that bears your name. See how striking it is here!"

Cerenkov did not go to Geneva. The Oak Ridge men made up for their disappointment by telling every visitor with great emphasis: "The blue glow that you see here was discovered by a Russian scientist." And if the visitor was from the Soviet Union, they would exchange a smile of pleasure with him, a sign of the good will that pervaded the conference.

The usefulness of the data collected during the construction and the testing of the Geneva reactor was not limited to Project Aquarium, or to future work at Oak Ridge. Scientists in all the countries taking advantage of President Eisenhower's offer of fissionable material were to benefit. One example may prove the truth of this statement: Tom Cole, the shy physicist who had awakened his wife to consult her about the reactor, had previously helped a Dutch scientist to calculate whether it would be possible to build the specific type of reactor the Dutch had in mind with the six kilograms of fissionable uranium available from the United States. At that time no reactor used 20 per cent enriched uranium as fuel, and it was not clear how fuel elements could be fabricated. The conservative estimates made by Tom Cole and the Dutch physicist left them in doubt. The reactor planned by the Dutch could be built and operated, but there was little margin left, and it seemed uncertain whether it would be advisable to undertake its construction. Then the Geneva reactor was built, and it used a smaller amount of fuel than was originally estimated. The calculations for the Dutch reactor were revised accordingly and showed that the quantity of fuel available would be ample.

The components of the Geneva reactor, packed in forty specially built crates and amounting to a total weight of about 30,500 pounds, were sent by truck to the Tyson McGhee Air Force Base at Knoxville, Tennessee, the closest city to Oak Ridge. By nine-thirty in the morning of June 30, two planes were ready on the ground: a C-54 and a huge C-124 Globemaster, one of the largest transport planes of the United States Air Force.

The Globemaster had swung open the big doors under its nose and had lowered its ramp, divided into two strips, each wide enough for the largest tire ever made. Fork-trucks shuttled busily in and out of the plane over this ramp; they inserted their two prongs under bulky crates, lifted them, drove up into the big belly of the Globemaster, and backed out empty. Another opening toward the tail was equipped with its own elevator to receive and lift smaller packages. The crate containing the control panel proved too large even for the fork-trucks: it was eighteen feet long, five feet wide, eight feet high, and looked like a huge monolith. It had to be hoisted up the ramp with winches and ropes.

The man on the ground who checked off the crates as they were loaded could not follow his long lists in order, from the first printed item to the last: the principles according to which the weight must be distributed inside a Globemaster did not necessarily follow the list prepared at Oak Ridge: the crew of the Military Air Transport System wanted the load distributed so that all the heavy boxes were not in one place; the Oak Ridge people wanted to make sure that, if an emergency arose and the crew decided to ditch part of the load, they would find only the less valuable items at hand near the exit door.

By three-thirty in the afternoon the forty crates were in their proper places inside the Globemaster; the crew and three guards had climbed in their cabin, above the space for the freight; eight more guards then took their seats in the C-54, together with the official "baby sitter" for the reactor, Dr. David Cope of the Oak Ridge Operations Office of the Atomic Energy Commission. The signal was then given, and the planes took off. They stopped for the last time in the United States at Dover, Delaware, where Dr. Cope showed the customs officers the first reactor export license ever issued.

While the reactor was being designed, constructed, assembled, and disassembled in Oak Ridge, it kept many persons busy in Washington, in New York, and in Switzerland. In Washington Dr. George G. Manov directed the reactor operations at the Atomic Energy Commission level. Each step in the reactor project meant at least a signature; Project Aquarium as a whole meant innumerable trips between Oak Ridge and Washington. But Dr. Manov belonged to that category of men who enjoy good food and are seldom upset— this second condition logically deriving from the first. It did not bother him to rush and to be rushed: he enjoyed the rides in the helicopter from Oak Ridge to the Knoxville airport; he accepted the airplane flights; he tolerated the limousine rides to the airport to meet men carrying blueprints or documents to be signed in a hurry and forwarded on the spot. But he was at his best when he could sit at his desk in front of the telephone and, receiver in hand, make decisions, advise others, and straighten out complications over long-distance lines.

In New York, the offices of Union Carbide and Carbon Corporation, operating the Oak Ridge Laboratory, arranged to ship many items by boat and train to Geneva. Two machines were necessary to operate the reactor: a motor generator and a water demineralizer. The electricity at Geneva was furnished at 220 volts, 50 cycles, while the equipment used for the reactor required power like our own, at 120 volts, 60 cycles; the generator was to convert the Swiss power to our requirements. A second motor generator, to be used as a spare, went on the Globemaster. It was loaded near the door among the items to be jettisoned, if necessary, since by that time the first generator was safely in Geneva.

The demineralizer was needed to remove all traces of mineral salts from the water used to fill the pool: minerals in the water would corrode the metal parts of the reactor; they would also become radioactive, constituting a hazard. The action of the demineralizer was illustrated in one of the panel exhibits prepared in New York for the reactor building. During the conference a woman visitor stopped in front of this panel, listened carefully to the guide's explanation of the demineralizer, and said: "I understand; this is a washing machine to wash water."

One of the busiest men at Union Carbide and Carbon Corporation in New York was Donald Stewart, a blond, mild-looking architect who would have been a musician if his father had not insisted on giving him a more remunerative education. As an architect he helped design the reactor exhibit. The scientists had never built a showpiece and did not know how to go about making a reactor into a display. When they asked for help, Union Carbide and Carbon Corporation passed the request on to Don Stewart, the firm's exhibits manager who specialized in three-dimensional selling. He might as well apply three dimensions to the problem of selling knowledge.

Don Stewart took his first trip to Oak Ridge on March 18 and spent ten hours there. He would have little time, the scientists warned him: whatever he proposed would have to be approved before four o'clock that same afternoon by Dr. Clarence Larson, Director of the Oak Ridge National Laboratory. Don Stewart set to work with the scientists. He had never seen a reactor, nor could he be shown one that day because the necessary clearance procedure would have delayed matters. So, sitting at a desk, he started to draw lines on paper following explanations he did not always understand; but, combining what he thought the scientists meant with his art, he soon made the drawing look like a reactor. "Where are you going to house it in Geneva?" he asked. That part of the project was well taken care of, the scientists answered. They could set up a prefabricated Army barracks. "An Army barracks on the grounds of the Palais des Nations! Impossible! Preposterous!" Mild-looking Donald Stewart had lost his mildness. He took a clean sheet of paper and in three minutes had the first *esquisse* for a more suitable building. By four o'clock his sketches were in Dr. Larson's office after having made the rounds of many desks. By four-twenty Don Stewart had obtained approval for his building, although it was to cost more than a barrack. He worked until late that evening at the reactor design, learned much physics without being aware of it, and returned to New York during the night.

He went back to Oak Ridge twice to discuss and design the panel exhibits. And there he ran into trouble. The scientists, wanting to sell *all* their knowledge, prepared lengthy explanations for each display; Don Stewart visualized an endless flow of visitors and thought it best to present only a digested survey. In the end, he said, the exhibits were not *quite* 100 per cent "long hair." He worked five days in Oak Ridge with Dr. Arthur Rupp, in charge of co-ordinating the exhibits, and prepared seventeen drawings so detailed that they looked like the photographs of the actual panels as they were later set up in Geneva. The drawings were hung in an Oak Ridge school building for official inspection and approved.

Back in New York Don Stewart set his exhibit builders at work, and four weeks later the crated exhibits were on the pier, ready to cross the ocean.

During this whole period, expediting communications between Washington, New York, Oak Ridge, and Geneva was a matter of prime importance. International relations were handled through normal diplomatic channels, and diplomatic pouch and mail services were at first used for all communications. Soon, however, even the air mail seemed too slow; instructions, inquiries, and replies were dispatched back and forth with such frequency that a serious bottleneck seemed likely to develop. Transatlantic telephone was resorted to. But in the final stages a teletype service was set up. A person sitting in an office could dictate a question to a teletype operator and in a few minutes receive an answer from all the way across the ocean. So Project Aquarium was quite appropriately helped by one of the very modern inventions.

The work in Oak Ridge, in Washington, and in New York would have been futile if at the same time the ground had not been prepared at Geneva, both figuratively and literally. The first negotiations with the Swiss government for permission to erect a reactor were carried out through official channels: Atomic Energy Commission—State Department—American Embassy in Bern—American

Consulate in Geneva—Swiss authorities. These negotiations revealed misgivings on the part of the Swiss about the health hazard
that might arise if a reactor were placed right in Geneva.

The Swiss people had little faith in the reassurances of our diplomats and were willing to trust only the word of Professor Paul Scherrer, the chairman of the Swiss Commission for Nuclear Research.
In order to talk with him and to discuss the matter in scientific
terms, Dr. Charles Winters, leader of Project Aquarium, flew to
Geneva from Oak Ridge in early March. The two scientists met together: a tall, thin American with chiseled features and mild appearance, bending down toward a medium-sized, strongly built
Swiss with a statuesque head sunk between broad shoulders. The
outcome of this interview was more than satisfactory, and the Swiss
people forgot their worries entirely. Later, during the two weeks of
the conference not only did they come in large crowds to see the
reactor erected by the Americans, but they leaned out over the pool;
a child, unobserved, stirred the shallow water above the lid with his
finger; another tried to dip a foot in it, and his shoe had to be tested
for contamination. But Professor Scherrer had been right; there was
no radioactivity on the shoe: the reactor was safe.

At the time when Dr. Winters received Swiss approval for his
project, he selected the most suitable spot in the gardens of the
Palais des Nations, believing that construction of the reactor building could start at once. A further complication arose, however, because of events dating back to the end of the First World War, when
the League of Nations was founded. The new organization had
selected Geneva for its headquarters and had purchased a beautiful
piece of land along the shores of Lake Leman. Before the League
had started any construction on this land, the authorities of the canton of Geneva expressed the wish to use it for a public park. The
canton owned a hill adjacent to these grounds, with a marvelous
view over the lake, better suited in their minds for a Palais; they
proposed to the League of Nations an exchange of properties. The
deal gave the League surface rights only. Thus it happened that the
United Nations, the heirs of the old League, legally owned only the
surface of their grounds. Dr. Winters could certainly build a chalet
for the reactor, as he had planned, but it was not clear at first
whether he could dig a hole for the tank. This difficulty was soon

ironed out, and the ground was broken on April 1. ("These Americans!" a Swiss remarked. "They can do anything. They come, they say 'We want a deep hole right in the grounds of the Palais des Nations,' and they get it.")

Anyone with some experience of both business and physicists will realize that it is virtually impossible for a physicist, even if as efficient as Dr. Winters, to go to a foreign country, deal with local labor, and turn out a building in three months. Several people and several circumstances were responsible for the achievement of this feat. Perhaps the weightiest of the circumstances was that Union Carbide and Carbon Corporation had a subsidiary in Geneva, Union Carbide Europa.

Some three weeks before Dr. Winters' arrival in Geneva, Mr. J. D. Conway, the director of Union Carbide Europa, had a telephone conversation about various business matters with the New York offices. He was casually told, among other things, that a reactor under construction in Oak Ridge would soon be flown to Geneva; that to house the reactor a building was needed; and that his help in smoothing the way for all phases of this project would be much appreciated.

Mr. Conway knew nothing about reactors; his firm operated mostly as sales agents and built nothing. Still, by the time Dr. Winters arrived in Geneva, Mr. Conway had prepared detailed reports on the reputation and abilities of several Swiss contractors; he had investigated possible involvements with the Swiss law; and provided assistance for doing business in Geneva. So Dr. Winters selected the contractor who, in his opinion, would do the best job in the shortest time: Conrad Zschokke. It did not matter that he had no written contract for the help hired, no money for advance payments. The United States government was going to pay in the end, and Uncle Sam's credit is good everywhere, despite his reputation for having his hands tied with red tape. The Swiss were as co-operative and worked as hard as if the Aquarium project were their own and they would receive the credit for its success.

The supervision of all work for the reactor building was intrusted to Mr. William L. Morgan, who had gone with Dr. Winters to Geneva from Oak Ridge, where he was technical assistant. Bill Morgan had taken along the sketch of the reactor building that Don

Stewart had hastily drawn in Oak Ridge; with that document as his only guide he gave the signal, and construction started on April 1. Constructions always start with excavations, and in this case the excavation was no minor job, for a deep hole was needed in which to place the tank for the reactor pool.

In the pictures taken shortly after the ground was broken, a spruce tree appeared very near to the place where the hole was being excavated. When the chalet was finished, the tree was not there. Had it been inclosed inside the building, or had it been chopped down? Neither was true. A gift to the United Nations from one of the member countries, the spruce tree had to be saved at all costs. Tied by wires that fastened it to the ground on a spot uphill from the chalet and attended by two loving tree experts, it waited sadly throughout the conference for the time when it could be reinstated in the place to which it had permanent rights.

One day, not long after work had started, a heavily loaded truck was approaching the site of construction when one of its wheels sank in the ground all the way to the axle. The puzzled workers went to see what had happened, dug around the wheel, and saw a hollow space underground. On the spur of the moment two men descended into the hole, with no gas lamp, no protective hats. They found a passage three hundred feet long, leading uphill and ending in a large room. There was excitement: perhaps a Roman basilica or a *palatium* had been discovered; and to think of a reactor on top of a Roman ruin! But no, the "room" was only a water cistern 150 years old, certainly no "antique" by European standards. Record of it was found on an old map of the city's water works.

When the hole was ready, with a little sand to soften its hard bottom, the huge steel tank, built in Geneva, was brought to the site with great care. It was tied with cables and then lifted, to be gently lowered into place. Then a cable snapped. The tank slid precipitously down into the hole. Bill Morgan and all the workers held their breath a moment: what if the tank had been damaged so badly that it would not hold water? Was this going to be the end of Project Aquarium? There was no time to build another tank.

Speculation is useless in such circumstances, and the experimental method prevailed. Bill Morgan filled the tank with water. The water did not drain away, but it was evident that the tank was tilted: the water reached the brim on one side and was a few inches below it on the opposite side. Because of the previous unfortunate experience it was felt that to lift the tank in order to straighten the foundation and then to lower the tank again was too dangerous an operation. Bill Morgan could not afford to try it. Instead, he sawed the top of the tank off and the brim became horizontal. The tank was still slanted, but Bill Morgan and the other members of the reactor crew kept the knowledge to themselves, and the public noticed nothing wrong.

After the tank had been installed, the building was erected around it. The Swiss are a sturdy people and they erected a sturdy chalet, adding their own ideas on construction to Don Stewart's concepts, as interpreted by Bill Morgan. The relations between the reactor's American crew and the Swiss workers were excellent at all times. The Swiss contractor had assigned the job of foreman to Michel Lorenz, a young Swiss who spoke English. Through him the Swiss learned something of the American way of life and the Americans became aware of some Swiss customs. Each respected the other: in the basement of the chalet facilities were soon installed for serving both coffee and wine. At first the Swiss workers kept their mid-morning and mid-afternoon activities secret, setting up their "Bar Atomique" in a hidden hole behind the tank. But once the cause of their mysterious disappearances from work became known, frequent invitations were exchanged between the "Coffee Room," run by the Oak Ridge guards in a corner of the basement, and the Swiss "Bar Atomique."

Coffee and wine did not slow down construction: with Oak Ridge scientists sweeping away metal filings from the bottom of the tank or climbing shaky ladders to give a hand at this and that, and with Swiss carpenters, electricians, riggers, and painters helping each other, the shell of the chalet was completed by June 16.

In Europe the putting-on of the roof of any building calls for celebration. Mr. Conway and Mr. Morgan entertained the construction and reactor teams at a large dinner party where much wine flowed and five Swiss francs reached the pocket of each Swiss worker, in the best of European traditions.

When on July 2 the Globemaster reached Geneva, twenty-seven hours after it had left Knoxville, the reactor building was ready to receive the precious cargo.

"We were wise," said the Oak Ridge scientists who came to Geneva to reassemble the reactor, "to put all parts in one plane. If an accident had occurred to the Globemaster we would have all gone home for a vacation. But if a smaller plane, with only a few of the crates, had been lost, we would again have worked eighteen hours a day, as in Oak Ridge, to rebuild the missing parts."

As it was, they worked only twelve hours a day under the direction and with the help of Dr. Winters. Since President Eisenhower was going to be in Geneva for the Big Four meeting, he should of course see our prize exhibit. So the crew did a month's work in two weeks. On July 17 Dr. Manov arrived from Washington; he alone had the authority to add the last fuel element to the reactor core. He gave the word, and on July 18 at 10:00 A.M. the reactor went critical; by coincidence, that was the very moment that the conference of the chiefs of government opened in the Palais des Nations, only a few yards away. The panel exhibits had just arrived, set up in units and all ready to be placed in the special openings designed for them.

Two days later the President of the United States came to pay his expected visit. The presidential party would not have been large, perhaps fifty people, but for a crowd of newspapermen and photographers who for the first time since the opening of the Big Four conference had a chance to come close to the President. So as he stood and looked at the reactor the photographers climbed on the simulator, on the showcases, on all the ladders the workmen were able to provide. A short camera man, with great foresight, had brought his own ladder and was the first to gain a vantage point high against a wall. Photographers were all over; if it had not been for the guards who pushed them back, they would not have respected even the platform on top of the reactor where the most delicate instruments were adjusted. A scientist later related with a grin that for the next few days he and his colleagues were kept busy washing finger marks off the walls and footprints—off the ceiling!

There was understandable confusion and noise in the chalet, but soon the scientists took President Eisenhower into the control room, behind the glass partition, through which the insatiable photographers could still get pictures. He was the greatest of the VIP's, about one hundred in all, who were allowed to operate the reactor in Geneva; he pushed the proper button and within five minutes the control rods were out, the instruments registered an increase of power, from zero slowly up to ten kilowatts and eventually to a hundred.

Genuinely interested in the marvelous contraption that caused uranium to yield its inner energy to man, President Eisenhower, now screened from the noise, could ask questions at will. There were in the control panel three red sticks like flattened Christmas candles, reproducing the motion of the control rods. Why did they not move at the same speed? How were radioisotopes produced in the pool? What did each instrument actually record? And the scientists explained: the control rods were withdrawn out of the reactor core slowly enough to keep the chain reaction in check, and one of them was raised even more slowly to give finer control. Radioisotopes were formed when the neutrons freed during the process of uranium fission were made to hit various substances; these substances could be placed in special capsules on a holder in the water near the core, and, after they had been irradiated a suitable time, they could be removed with special long tongs. Pneumatic tubes with compressed air could also be used to place light aluminum capsules inside or outside the core.

As the President emerged from the control room, he made ready to speak and immediately the noise gave way to perfect silence.

"I am very grateful to the experts in charge of this building," President Eisenhower said, "for conducting me through. . . . I am very pleased that our country is able here to establish this reactor to help the scientists of the world to make progress along the lines of peaceful use of atomic energy. . . . I hope that private business and professional men throughout the world will take an interest, and provide an incentive in finding ways in which this new science can be used. In the meantime, I hope that everybody who gets a chance to see this [reactor], will learn that there are really many, many ways in which atomic science can be used for the benefit of mankind and not destruction. . . ."

President Eisenhower's visit to the reactor building lasted forty-five minutes and left everybody in high spirits.

His expression of hope that private business and professional men would provide an incentive to finding ways in which atomic science could be used bore fruit quickly. Inspired by it, Henry Ford II and his two brothers, Benson and William Clay Ford, established a one million dollar fund for "Atoms for Peace Awards," which was announced by Admiral Strauss the opening day of the conference. The Ford brothers proposed the fund and the awards as a memorial to their father and grandfather, Edsel B. and Henry Ford. According to the provisions of this proposal, an international jury of awards, appointed each year, would select among the world's scientists, inventors, and engineers the individual or group of individuals who made the greatest contribution to the peaceful uses of atomic energy in that year. The yearly award was to be 75,000 dollars.

From the end of July a different sort of activity went on at the chalet. Dr. François Kertesz, a Hungarian-born chemist from Oak Ridge, held a "reactor school for guides." Seven girl students from the Geneva school for interpreters, each of whom knew at least four languages, were hired to lead the visitors through the reactor exhibits and give them explanations in the language they desired. The girls had hardly ever heard the word "reactor" and they knew no technical terminology. So Dr. Kertesz, who could speak six languages, undertook the task of drilling the future guides in atomic engineering. They looked bored and tired at the end of the first lesson; what pretty girl cares to know about reactors and how they work? But there must have been something infectious in the Oak Ridge men's enthusiasm for their Project Aquarium; it had spread already from them to the Swiss who had collaborated in the construction of the building or had helped assemble the reactor. It now spread to the seven girls, and they came to take as much pride in the success of the reactor exhibits as the Oak Ridge scientists themselves. The scientists had nothing but praise for the girls, for their looks and their efficiency. The girls had one complaint against the Oak Ridge National Laboratory: it had sent only married men.

Several Ph.D.'s in laboratory coats were always present for discussions on a higher scientific level with their peers from every part of the world, if they could find a language in common. But the less demanding general public was left to the girls. From August 7, when the exhibits were opened to the public, until the evening of August 21, when they were finally closed, the girls took care of well over sixty thousand visitors, hurrying to guide group after group in the summer heat that was heightened by the crowd inside; switching from one language to another; reverting to English to seek the help of the Ph.D.'s, if asked questions that they could not answer; too proud of their newly acquired knowledge ever to be willing to cut down explanations and shorten the tours. Scientists, incognito, listened intently: Wigner, the father of the swimming pool reactor, received one girl's full lecture with unflinching eyes. Zinn, the director of Argonne National Laboratory, was said to have asked questions in broken English, thus hiding his identity, and to have received satisfactory answers.

The reactor and the technical exhibits were reserved for the delegates to the conference until four in the afternoon, and then they were opened to the public. At that hour large crowds streamed down the hill from Porte XIV, toward the reactor building, where they lined up on the stairs leading to the entrance, three or four abreast, as if they were going to a special performance at a fashionable theater. Whole families came together: mothers leading their children by the hand, fathers carrying the youngest on their shoulders. They chattered. "It smells," said a girl in French, sniffing the new chalet's strong scent of pine and tar. "It is the smell of the atom," replied her father.

Inside, most of the visitors showed real interest: they crowded around the pool and remained a long time in front of the showcases. Many took notes, on pads or on the pages of the reactor booklet handed out at the door in four editions, one in each of the four official languages. Young inventors-to-be turned all the knobs on the simulator, which was found out of adjustment at the end of each visiting period.

One day among the visitors to the reactor there came a small white-haired man who spoke little English and had a strong German accent. After he had made the tour of the chalet and had duly expressed his admiration for the attractive reactor, he asked to operate it. But the Oak Ridge men were very jealous of their control room.

A list of the few VIP's to be allowed in it had been prepared in advance. When they came to visit, they were treated with great ceremony and watched closely: the time the President of the Swiss Confederation, Max Petitpierre, had started the reactor, two scientists had leaned over him to see that he did not push the wrong button. The German visitor's appearance, quiet and withdrawn, gave no indication that he was a man of consequence. To stave him off, his guide told him that the instruments were terribly delicate, the operation difficult, and so on. "In the past I have worked a little with fission myself," the German ventured mildly. He was Professor Otto Hahn, head of the German delegation, who had discovered fission with Strassmann in 1939 in Berlin. He *did* operate the reactor!

The Geneva reactor became the property of the Swiss government on August 22. Switzerland, the first country to acquire a research reactor under President Eisenhower's Atoms for Peace program, purchased slightly used merchandise, but at the bargain price of 180,000 dollars including the chalet and its contents. The reactor parts alone, as shipped from Oak Ridge with no housing and no showcases, had been valued at 340,000 dollars. The deal was satisfactory to both sides. President Eisenhower had previously announced that under bilateral agreements the United States would sell research reactors to friendly countries at half their cost. Thus our government was receiving a fair, if somewhat low, price for the Geneva reactor. Besides, the Oak Ridge team was very happy to be relieved of the responsibility for restoring the grounds to their previous condition and, even more, not to have to return the spruce tree to its place: the Swiss agreed to do all this, pleased as they were with what they were getting, without even having to send a mission to our country. They also agreed to pay a 4 per cent interest on the leased fuel, valued at twenty-five dollars per gram of uranium 235 contained in it.

The signing of the agreement took place in the reactor building on August 20 at a formal ceremony in which five persons participated: Switzerland was represented by Professor Paul Scherrer, Chairman of the Swiss Commission for Nuclear Research, and by Walter Boveri, Chairman of the Board of Directors of the government-supported company "Reacteur, S.A.," which was to operate the reactor after it had reached its final home at Wurenlingen, a village near Zurich; for the United States there were Chairman Strauss, Commissioner Libby, and Miss Frances E. Willis, Ambassador to Switzerland.

They all sat on a bench, Ambassador Willis in the middle with two of the men on each side, all turning their backs to the reactor; they made brief speeches and looked uncomfortable: wherever Chairman Strauss went in Geneva, television cameras never failed to follow, and so it happened this time. Pitiless lights shone in the faces of the five people sitting in a row, a new torture brought to the innocent by the modern techniques of information mediums. Every time the five thought the eye of the television camera was not seeing them, they averted their faces for a brief second and then again submitted resignedly to the ordeal.

Two days later the reactor chalet was the seat of a much less formal ceremony, a farewell party for all the members of the reactor team. The ever present cameras recorded only happy faces: gay scientists carrying a large bilingual sign on a wooden pole—"Vendu —Sold"; under the French word "Vendu" someone had scribbled "Pas Cher" ("not at high price"). The happy-looking men could not fail to be sad at heart. This was the end of Project Aquarium. The reactor in which they had united their efforts since early in March; the building which since early July they had hardly left for more than the night hours; all the things that for two strenuous weeks had been principals in the reactor drama were no longer theirs. In all likelihood they would never see them again.

8 RUSSIAN SCIENTISTS IN GENEVA

It is a common trait of the human mind to expect the unknown to be strange, or at least different from what is known. The mind is seldom conscious of this expectation and even more seldom is it able to express or give definite shape to what it does expect. Yet the expectation exists and is strong enough to impart flavor to the unknown even after it has been revealed and found commonplace. If they had been questioned before the opening of the conference, the United States delegates would hardly have admitted that they expected the Russians to be different from themselves; but subconsciously they were prepared to find differences rather than similarities. After meeting the Soviets, they remarked upon and stressed those Soviet traits and qualities that they found to be like our own. They spoke of this likeness with gratification and a bit of wonder, as one may speak of a new and unexpectedly pleasant discovery.

Typical of this was the attitude of an American who was working at our technical exhibit in the Palais des Nations. Having often peeked in at the Russian exhibit, he had learned to recognize some of the Russian workers by sight. He had got into the habit of going to the United Nations private beach during the lunch hour to take a long swim and a sunbath and to eat his lunch there. He realized that some of the Russian workers did exactly the same; he saw them on the beach carrying their lunch, apparently enjoying the waters of the lake and the sunshine, and biting with healthy appetites into their sandwiches. Months later, when the American related the episode, his candor and his wide-open and shining eyes indicated that he was still surprised.

Some of our older delegates, especially those of European origin, had met a few Russian physicists and chemists in the early thirties; but to the younger Americans the Russian scientist was an unknown specimen. Unknown also were Soviet achievements in atomic science, for the secrecy due to the Second World War, and later to the cold war, had stopped English publication of Russian papers right at the time when the atomic field was being explored.

Conjectures about the state of Soviet knowledge were lively in Geneva. The questions: "What will the Russians disclose? What will they have to show? How freely will they speak?" were the ones most frequently asked from table to table on the terrace in front of the Hôtel du Rhône from the day the United States delegation started to gather in Geneva. The Hotel Metropole, where the Russian delegation was housed, was on the other side of the lake out of sight of the Hôtel du Rhône. The first encounters between Americans and Russians took place at the Palais des Nations. Our scientists were impressed less by the Soviet delegates' reserve and restraint during the first few days than by the ease and friendliness that they soon displayed, and by their scientific achievements, which in many ways were like our own.

As an act of courtesy George Weil invited the Russian scientists working at their technical exhibit to visit ours several days before they were opened to the public. A small group arrived for the visit, led by Professor Ryabchikov, in charge of the Soviet exhibit. They had their interpreter with them, Mr. Dennysenkov, a heavy-set youth with a jolly face, who spoke technical English fluently and who later was seen wherever any Russians went. George Weil had engaged the assistance of Rita Liepina, a Latvian-born librarian from the Library of Congress in Washington, who was in Geneva to work at our technical library. She could speak some Russian but was in awe of the scientific terms that she might be asked to translate.

The visit proceeded with strain and with no warmth. Only two of the Russians, Professor Ryabchikov and another, both somewhat older and clearly more important than the rest, asked questions. They wanted to know whether the fuel elements on display actually contained uranium and how much; they asked for specific data on size of components and energy output of reactors; they listened to the answers with no comment, with no change of expression, as if afraid of revealing their thoughts. They showed some interest in the items on display but none in the few United States delegates who were present, or in the scientists in charge of the exhibits, who answered questions freely and volunteered information.

Even these seemingly inscrutable Russians showed human reactions and broke out in cheerful bursts of laughter when they operated the "magic hands" or manipulators, designed for remote han-

dling of radioactive substances. The Soviet delegates learned that
the manipulators have "feeling" when they found that they could
grab tiny bottles on a shelf two or three yards away beyond a thick
window, pull the corks, and then put the bottles down where they
chose, and that all the time they were in perfect control of these
actions.

A larger group of Soviet technicians working at the Russian exhibit, led by Professor Ryabchikov, visited the United States swimming pool reactor two days before its official opening. They were
young and kept close together; they stood a long while near the railing of the pool and stared seriously at the water, unsmiling, somewhat stiff in their too-wide trousers. Their intent expression gave
their faces a peculiar quality of utter stillness. They asked few questions but listened to the explanations of the reactor personnel, translated by the same Mr. Dennysenkov, the chunky interpreter who had
previously been at the technical exihibits. Professor Ryabchikov was
then invited to operate the reactor. Taken by surprise, he lost his
inscrutableness and let his face express his emotions: amazement
and uncertainty between the wish to accept and the fear that something might go wrong if he accepted. But he did, and all was well.

As soon as the conference got under way and all the scientists met
and mingled in the marble halls of the Palais des Nations, as soon as
the national groups broke up and lost their identity in favor of the
individuals, the Russians loosened up and became typical scientists
eager to learn and teach, displaying common human feelings when
work allowed time for them. Scientific matters had priority, but personal subjects also came up in conversations. Viktor Vavilov had
brought along a picture of his wife and two children taken in a
forest near Moscow, and in showing it he appeared as proud as any
husband and father in the West. He was seen one morning rushing
around in great excitement: his wife, who had overcome the difficulties of red tape and obtained a passport, was to have arrived in
Geneva but had gone to Zurich by mistake, with no money and little
knowledge of languages other than Russian—the wife, of course, was
soon rescued and taken to Geneva.

The ties binding Russian families together seem stronger than
ours. Families keep closer together; children live with parents and
grandparents, uncles and aunts—the housing shortage, still very

acute in cities like Moscow, may have something to do with fostering this condition. Sons seem to follow in their fathers' footsteps oftener than in the United States. Vavilov was a scientist's son and so was Marcov, a red-haired young physicist with an engaging smile.

Dr. Vladimirski, a Russian physicist with a thick shock of wavy hair springing from his forehead, missed his six-and-a-half-year-old son and wanted to talk about him. Asked whether the child went to school, he said that in Russia children started school when they were seven years old, and, trying to explain in English that for younger children there were kindergartens, he said: "We have other types of institutions for such people." In these "institutions" working mothers could leave "such people," their young children, all day long and also day and night for as long as a week, if the mothers were assigned to some special project.

Delegates from both sides of the Iron Curtain had several chances of meeting at the "socials," the receptions given by various delegations. The socials were all well attended and crowded, but the Soviet party was the best attended and the most crowded of all. One must conclude that none of those invited relinquished the unique opportunity to see Russian hosts and to taste Russian vodka, and that all accepted the invitation. So far as it could be ascertained, only a few wives missed the occasion; the Russians had planned a stag party but changed their minds at the last moment and circulated invitations to the wives by word of mouth. Some of the ladies were not reached in time, and some felt offended by the lateness of the invitation. The Russians were not alone in remembering the wives only at the last moment: the British also issued invitations for their party to delegates only, and then later extended them to wives. There was greater justification for the omission in the case of the Russians, for none of them had their wives along—Mrs. Vavilov joined her husband in Geneva, but only for the last two days of the conference.

The Soviet reception was held at the Hotel Metropole. The receiving line, made up exclusively of men, was headed by Academician Skobeltzin, the tall, imposing, white-haired Soviet member of the Advisory Committee, a vice-president of the conference, and head of the Soviet delegation. The others in the receiving line were not known to the United States scientists. In the two rooms where long refreshment tables had been set up the atmosphere was jovial. The crowd pressed along the tables; the hosts, cheerful and pleasant, were kept busy filling plates with tidbits and fruit, glasses with vodka and white wine. Caviar, the hope of which had not been the least attraction, was scanty, but wine and cordiality made up for its lack of abundance. A small, lively man helped entertain and passed plates around as if he considered himself a member of the household; he was Mr. Boris Lifschitz, head of the three-man delegation from the tiniest republic in the world, San Marino, which had gone Communist at the last elections although its fourteen thousand inhabitants were good, churchgoing Catholics.

A group of women delegates from various countries had a chance to meet at a small tea party given by Miss Marquis, correspondent of the *Los Angeles Times*, in the roof restaurant of the Palais des Nations. Women are said to be sensitive to natural beauty, but on that occasion the women delegates disregarded it. In front of them lay the blue lake, its green shores dotted with villas, beyond which was the impressive peak of Mont Blanc; but the women did not look at the scenery, because three of them were Russian and it was a novel treat for all of them to be together. Perhaps the two British women, the French women, and the two from the United States (Miss Marquis and this historian), stilled by curiosity and shyness, would have sat staring at the Russians indefinitely. It was the Soviet ladies who enlivened the party.

They came to the party together, smiling, bubbling with friendliness. They took the others by the arm and said how much they had wanted to meet them. The tallest of the Russians, mannish looking, with blond unruly hair and dark-rimmed glasses, told the others by way of introducing herself that she had a twenty-four-year-old daughter who she wished would marry soon because she wanted grandchildren. This quite international feeling put everyone at ease, and the conversation became lively. Science was mentioned only to explain the task of each at the conference. Except for the two Americans, all the others were working in the exhibits. The woman who wanted grandchildren was a mineralogist; she spoke only a little English, just enough to talk about her daughter, who was a historian at the Kremlin, and to explain that the Kremlin had been recently opened to the public; later, perhaps tired by the effort, she preferred to talk through a woman interpreter who had meanwhile joined the party. The second Russian woman was a jovial, witty chemist who spoke sufficiently fluent English to crack jokes and hardly ever stopped her pleasant chatter. The third was a quiet, younger biologist with dark hair and large dreamy eyes.

They told of their home lives and of the crowded conditions in Moscow; they said proudly that a co-operative apartment building was under construction for scientific workers like themselves and that soon they would enjoy more home space. They had read many English books: "Of course they are available in our libraries," they said. Then they asked what modern Russian authors the other women knew. The British, French, and American women exchanged blank glances and answered, "None."

Most of our delegates, fond as they seemed of parties, drew greater satisfaction from scientific exchanges with the Russians than from the socials. Informal meetings of various kinds between scientists from both sides of the Iron Curtain were arranged during the two weeks of the conference. Many of the Soviet delegates knew a little English; some Western scientists knew some Russian and acted as interpreters. The busiest of the unofficial interpreters was Professor John Turkevich, of Princeton University, who, being of Russian extraction, spoke and understood that language perfectly. He was called upon on many occasions, often several times a day, and usually was entirely exhausted from his arduous task when he went back to his room and to his wife at the Hôtel du Rhône. Professor Victor F. Weisskopf of the Massachusetts Institute of Technology also knew some Russian. He was Austrian-born and felt strongly drawn to do all he could to improve relations between East and West. A third interpreter was a British theoretical physicist, the friend of a large number of Americans: Professor Rudolf Peierls, who had been a member of the British delegation in Los Alamos that during the war had helped United States scientists in the research and development of the atomic bomb.

Weisskopf and Peierls were the promoters of informal theoretical seminars. At their request the scientific secretaries of the United Nations made available a hall and even a blackboard, probably the only blackboard in the whole Palais des Nations. In this hall, for three successive half-days, thirty to thirty-five people from Russia,

Yugoslavia, Czechoslovakia, and from the West came together to discuss topics of theoretical physics: nuclear structure, meson physics, and field theory. Professor Weisskopf chaired the meetings. English was spoken, slowly and clearly. When someone did not understand, he raised a hand, and Weisskopf called upon Peierls to translate.

Victor Weisskopf was extremely gratified by these seminars, which he called "a resounding success" and "the most important thing I have ever done." Weisskopf remarked that the collaboration between the Russian experimentalists and theoreticians was strikingly evident and very remarkable. Professor Veksler, who was a Russian experimentalist and a specialist in accelerators, attended the theoretical seminars and displayed comprehension of theories to a degree not always found among experimentalists. Professor Blokhintsev, a prominent theoretical physicist, had worked two years on reactors; at the conference he presented two theoretical papers and also the eagerly awaited one on "The First Atomic Power Station of the U.S.S.R. and the Prospect of Atomic Power Development." Professor Blokhintsev, bald, quiet, wearing a silk-lapeled morning coat to deliver this important paper at a general session, personified the type of dignified, formal professor, once so often found in European universities.

Other encounters between East and West were not as organized as the theoretical seminars and took place in more casual fashion. Often delegates decided to stay on in the lecture halls after the sessions were over to discuss informally the topics which had been formally presented in the papers. A number of luncheons and dinners were arranged for the benefit of small groups interested in specific fields of science. The first of the luncheons took place at the restaurant on the eighth floor of the Palais des Nations. It had been called for twelve noon, but at that time only the United States and British guests had arrived, among them Professor Weisskopf and Dr. Donald J. Hughes, of the Brookhaven National Laboratory. After a while they began to doubt that the Russians were ever going to come. Captain Maxwell of the Pergamon Press took matters in hand. He went around, made telephone calls, and located the Soviet guests.

There was an hour's delay in the luncheon, and even then for the first twenty minutes it looked as if the delay and trouble had not been worth going through. The Russians were sitting at a table with Western men for the first time; they were shy and silent. Then Dr. Eugene Rabinowitch of the University of Illinois, a Russian-born, easygoing, easy-talking man, joined the party. In a few minutes the Russians thawed; they talked of their families, told jokes about their wives and about the difficulties between theoreticians and experimentalists. Despite these pleasant topics, what made Russians and Americans really fraternize was the discussion of cross-sections, in the layman's opinion one of the least interesting subjects of modern physics.

In nuclear physics, "cross-section" is the measure of the statistical probability that a specific nuclear event will take place. Thus the absorption cross-section of uranium 238 for slow neutrons is the measure of the probability that a nucleus of uranium 238 will capture a slow neutron. A cross-section is expressed as an area, and is defined as the effective area presented by a single target nucleus to the bombarding particles. The unit of cross-section is the "barn": according to a widely circulated story, a physicist, much impressed by the size of a cross-section, once exclaimed: "But it is as large as a barn!" and barn it remained. It has become an international term and may be seen printed in Cyrillic characters in Russian books and publications.

Absorption and fission cross-sections for uranium isotopes and for plutonium are among the most important data in reactor science. They were kept secret in all countries where they had been measured. All countries declassified them for the Geneva conference. The United States went further: a book filled with data and graphs on cross-section values obtained by American workers was included in the set of eight volumes of selected reference material presented to each foreign delegation.

The cross-section volume was prepared by Donald Hughes, one of the Americans at the luncheon at which the Russians were one hour late. Don Hughes was proud of this volume, as elegantly bound as the other seven and twice as large, and of the typical American barn on its frontispiece. The barn, he humorously explained, would indicate that the book was on cross-sections even to those who could read no English! He was even prouder of the paper-bound addendum attached to the cross-section book, because it contained cross-section values obtained in other countries.

When Don Hughes had first thought of this addendum, he had sought foreign data through the scientific secretaries of the United Nations. To approach the Russians had seemed an adventure. Who knew anything at that time of Russian physicists and of what their reaction to a request for data might be? Viktor Vavilov, Deputy Secretary-General for the conference, and Nikolai Dobrotin, scientific secretary, were invited to Brookhaven. Hughes told them of his idea, of his hope for their co-operation; the two Soviet physicists agreed to come back to Brookhaven and bring the cross-section data collected in the Soviet Union. They did.

There had been hope and some apprehension on the part both of the Russians and of the Americans: what if the values were far apart? But they matched. The Russians had been concerned about a little jag in one of their curves. They thought it might be due to inaccuracy of measurements. The same little jag was in the corresponding curve of values found in the United States. Astounding!

At the conference physicists from France, England, Russia, and the United States presented papers on cross-sections, discussed them, compared values. The agreement was excellent. Pleasure and excitement mounted. Not that the scientists were too surprised to find that plutonium and uranium behaved in the same way in all countries! Yet, the agreement was proof that their work was good and their results were correct. Groups of independent researchers had obtained the same values; this was a fact to be proud of. It also indicated that truth cannot be hidden, that secrecy does not prevent progress in science in other countries but, instead, causes a duplication of efforts, which, if pooled, could be spent with better profit.

In Geneva an informal group of specialists in cross-section measurements from the United States, England, France, and Russia prepared a set of values representing the best average of data from all countries. This was greatly to facilitate reactor design everywhere.

To avoid misunderstandings and delays, all luncheons and dinners after the first one were arranged through Dr. Paul McDaniel. If some of our delegates wished to ask Soviet scientists to a meal, Dr.

McDaniel would call the secretariat of the Soviet delegation at the Hotel Metropole and specify names, time, and place. The Russians, always eager to return any courtesy received, sent invitations by messenger to McDaniel's office, and thus an easy channel was provided to arrange for people staying in different parts of town to get together.

One of the most memorable dinner parties took place at a fashionable French restaurant in Geneva, where ". . . the wine was the very best and it contributed to a very friendly and congenial evening," as Professor Ernest O. Lawrence of the University of California later recalled in a letter to a friend. With Lawrence were his university colleague Professor Glenn T. Seaborg, and Professor John Turkevich, who was ready to act as interpreter if the need should arise. The three of them were among the tallest men in our delegation, and perhaps with the exception of Dr. Seaborg, who was somewhat thinner and lanky, they were also the most robust-looking. "The arrangement was to stop by the Hotel Metropole to pick them up," Professor Lawrence stated in his letter, "but when we arrived we found they wanted to follow us in their own car."

"They" were Professors Veksler and Vinogradov and their interpreter. Vinogradov and Seaborg were experts in transuranic chemistry; Veksler and Lawrence, in accelerating machines. Lawrence was the man who invented the cyclotron, a machine in which charged particles, like protons and deuterons, are made to go round and round in a magnetic field at an always increasing pace and are thus accelerated to high energies; for this invention Lawrence received the Nobel Prize in 1939. Veksler was the author of a principle applied in most modern descendants of the original cyclotron built after the Second World War, such as synchrotrons, synchro-cyclotrons, cosmotrons, and bevatrons. According to Veksler's principle, the energy of the charged particles in an accelerating machine can be greatly increased beyond the values previously reached by adjusting the strength or the frequency of the accelerating voltage. Veksler published his principle in 1944 in a Russian journal, which was not read in the West. A few months later Edwin McMillan of Berkeley, unaware of Veksler's work, reached the same conclusions and published a paper in which he presented the same principle. Veksler protested and brought his work to the West's attention; McMillan at once acknowledged Veksler's priority.

To Western scientists in Geneva, Veksler, from a mere name attached to a principle, became a real man in the flesh: small, dapper, with long smooth hair, and with eyeglasses below a spacious forehead. He and Lawrence were to share an evening lecture period on accelerating machines. It was quite natural that at the dinner party which gave Lawrence his first chance to talk with his Russian counterpart he should ask Veksler "after a toast or two and perhaps a few hors d'oeuvres . . . what he was going to talk about in his evening lecture."

"He told me that he was among other things going to describe and show pictures of their new synchro-phasotron, which is Russian for bevatron."

The bevatron, the most recent of Lawrence's accelerating machines and the largest currently in operation in the United States, was built at the Radiation Laboratory in Berkeley; its name came from the newly created term "bev" meaning "billion electron volts." Another accelerator of this type was the cosmotron at Brookhaven National Laboratory.

Veksler's mention of a synchro-phasotron aroused Lawrence's interest, as evidenced in his letter: "I said that sounds very interesting and asked him to tell me about it. He said it could produce 10 billion volt protons (ours produces 6.2 billion volt protons), and that the magnet has 36,000 tons of steel (ours has 9,000 tons). Of course you can imagine that was a real surprise to Glenn and me."

It was a surprise to the entire scientific world.

"The next Thursday, when we gave our evening lectures," Lawrence went on, "I spoke first and showed slides of our bevatron and was followed by Veksler and he showed slides of theirs, which looked very much like ours only it was bigger."

So the Soviet Union had the largest accelerator in the world! It was not quite completed, according to Veksler and to his slides, but almost and was due to be in full operation within a year. Its magnet consisted of four quadrants separated by gaps eight meters long, and disposed to form a circle of twenty-eight meters' radius. A power of 140,000 kilowatts was needed to operate it. This power would have been sufficient to supply electricity to a town of 140,000 people, for normal power consumption is about one kilowatt per person. To duplicate this machine in the United States would cost about **sixty million dollars.**

The synchro-phasotron was not the first surprise provided by Russia in the field of the accelerating machines. The previous March the Soviets had slightly lifted the curtain on their research in pure nuclear physics and announced work done with a synchro-cyclotron, which they called a phasotron. This is a type of machine that accelerates protons to high energies. The Russian synchro-cyclotron, of which nobody had heard a single word up to the spring of 1955, was the largest and the most potent of its kind in the world. It accelerated protons to the energy of 680 million electron volts.

Strictly speaking, accelerating machines are not related to the production or applications of atomic energy. They were not on the topical agenda and were not discussed in any of the conference sessions. But they were chosen as a topic for evening lectures in recognition of the fact that they are the most powerful tool made by man to investigate the nature of atomic nuclei and elementary particles. The fundamental knowledge that has been and will be acquired through these investigations might very likely affect future practical applications of atomic energy.

More powerful machines were under construction or being planned in the United States and at the European Center of Nuclear Research in Geneva. It is interesting to note that these machines were to use smaller magnets than the synchro-phasotron to produce higher energies, because of the application of the "strong focusing" principle. This was discovered after the bevatron, the cosmotron, and the Soviet synchro-phasotron had already been designed. The accelerator at the European Center was to use six thousand tons of iron to produce an estimated energy of twenty to twenty-five bev, while the synchro-phasotron used thirty-six thousand tons of iron to produce ten bev.

These considerations may illustrate the reasons for Lawrence's interest in what Veksler revealed at dinner. In the already quoted letter, Lawrence said about his two new friends: "In our talks with Veksler and Vinogradov that evening, we found them very polite, very courteous and friendly and apparently quite free to discuss anything they wished. We discussed a great many things, of course, and I was impressed with their competence as scientists, and they seemed to me also to be gentlemen in every sense of the word. . . . They told us something of the large number of scientists they have working in Russia and the even larger numbers that are being trained. . . . They also told us they had practically unlimited funds for scientific research. . . ."

Many other of our delegates were impressed with the number of Russian scientists and science students. In Geneva, where optimism and friendly feelings prevailed, this large number was a reason for admiration. Later it caused concern in some quarters. It was estimated that between 1950 and 1960 Soviet Russia would have graduated 1,200,000 scientists and engineers and the United States 900,-000. This fact was considered an indication that the United States might lose its lead in science and technology unless the problem of finding better high-school and college teachers of science and of attracting more students in this field was attacked vigorously and solved rapidly. In the Soviet Union, scientists were the highest paid class after the politicians: most of them owned two cars and a cottage in the country.

Transuranics, which were Seaborg's and Vinogradov's field, did their part in furthering good relations between Americans and Russians. "Transuranic" is a term applied to all elements that come after uranium in the periodic table of elements. Until the time, after the discovery of artificial radioactivity, when scientists began creating elements not found in nature, uranium was the heaviest and the last element in the periodic table. Its atomic number is 92. Immediately after the Second World War, two man-made transuranic elements were announced: neptunium and plutonium, respectively of atomic numbers 93 and 94. More transuranics were later created, and their creation disclosed. In Geneva Professor Seaborg, chairing the session on the chemistry of transuranics, announced the names of elements 99, 100, and 101, according to the well-established practice that discoverers of new elements have the privilege of naming them. The names were respectively fermium, einsteinium, and mendelevium, in honor of Enrico Fermi, Albert Einstein, and the Russian Dimitri Mendeleev, who established the periodic table of elements in 1868. Dr. Seaborg said that mendelevium was named to indicate the importance of the periodic table in the discovery of new elements. Russian scientists, touched by the recognition given to Mendeleev, declared that they would adopt all Western names of transuranics, changing those that had been different in Russia.

Soon after the Russians had visited our exhibits before the open-ing of the conference, they returned the kindness and asked our dele-gates to a preview of theirs. Unlike most of the exhibiting countries, the Soviets had no commercial display at the Palais des Expositions but had concentrated their efforts in their technical exhibition at the Palais des Nations.

Some of our people had been intrigued by the large number of crates with incomprehensible Russian words printed on them that piled up by a side entrance of the Palais des Nations during the last week of July. For some days they looked abandoned; nothing was done with them. Then, about a week before the conference started, a crew of about twenty workers arrived from Russia and joined forces with locally hired Swiss labor. The noise and din of wrenches and of pounding hammers pervaded the two halls assigned to the Soviets' display. Guards at the doors turned back curious onlookers, but not before they had managed to peek in. All who had a chance to come near the Russian workers submitted them to the same scrutiny all Russians underwent in Geneva. The workers, possibly because they too, like the scientists, felt the eyes of the world on them, seemed overly silent, almost sullen and dour. But when one day Viktor Vavilov spoke to them in their own language, giving encour-agement and orders at the same time, their faces lit up, and they smiled at Vavilov and went back to their work with new ardor. And the exhibits, which they had ready on time, were quite remarkable.

When our scientists visited the Soviet exhibits, they were shown around by two interpreters, the always present chunky young man and a slight, dark-haired woman. The guided tour started in the en-trance hall of the exhibit where two large, museum-like showcases contained a spectacular collection of the most important uranium minerals and ores. It was later remarked that no indication was given of the place where these samples were found. During the entire conference no information at all was released on the location or ex-tent of uranium and thorium deposits in the Soviet Union.

From the entrance hall the guides took our scientists into the main hall, from the walls of which four large pictures looked down: Lenin, Bulganin, Mendeleev, and Pavlov, the well-known physiologist on whose theories most of the Russian biological papers were based. Three reactor models were in the middle of the hall. Two of them were research reactors; the third drew the greatest interest since it reproduced the Soviet atomic power plant. It was housed in a neo-classic building with pillars and cornices; and when the Russians were asked why they had chosen a style so ill suited for a modern industrial establishment, they shrugged their shoulders, saying: "You know the architects! We had to do what they wanted!" Our scientists commented that the same problems arose everywhere.

The guidebook of the U.S.S.R. exhibit, an elegant brochure with green and yellow cover trimmed with gold, available in the four official languages, said in part about this plant: "The 5,000 kw atomic power station of the USSR Academy of Sciences is the Soviet Union's first industrial power station operating on nuclear energy.

"The power station was commissioned on June 27, 1954, and has generated about 15 million kw in the course of operation.

"The atomic power station was built specially to gain scientific and engineering know-how in the future designing and building of large atomic power stations. . . . Apart from supplying industries with electricity the plant provides . . . for a current comprehensive aforethought programme of scientific and engineering research. . . .

"The principal components of the power plant equipment are: 1. The nuclear reactor. 2. The heat exchanger in which the steam is produced. 3. The steam turbine. . . .

". . . the nuclear reactor . . . is a thermal-neutron graphite reactor with graphite moderator. . . . The fuel channels contain tubular uranium slugs which are cooled by circulating water. Heat generated by uranium fission warms the water in the pipes. . . . The graphite masonry of the reactor is contained in a steel cylinder, . . . forming a hermetic shell, which may be filled with inert gas, non-antagonistic to graphite. . . ."

The reactor plant and its operation were particularly well illustrated in a movie that was said to be the best, from the production angle, of the many technical films shown at the conference. It was called "First in the World" because the plant was the first to produce electricity steadily and feed it to power lines for civilian use. (In the United States electricity had been generated by several reactors but had not been fed into the lines as early as in the Soviet Union.) The movie was in color, with an accompaniment of excellent recorded music. It showed in detail the reactor core, its 128 fuel elements and the 22 control rods; the crane used to lift the spent elements out of the reactor and to replace them with fresh ones; the remote controls by which white-coated and white-capped personnel operated the crane; and the detection devices used in the plant. It showed also how the electricity generated in the turbine was distributed and put to use; thus, on a collective farm, cows were shown being milked by atomic power.

In short, the movie was an excellent visual aid for the material on this plant presented at the conference "in sufficient detail," according to the guidebook, "for any country interested in building a similar type plant of greater power on the basis of the experience accumulated." Soviet scientists said that a much larger version of this plant was under construction in their country. There was no indication either on the model or in the movie of the location of the power plant. But, when asked, the Russians said readily that it was near Podolsk, southeast of Moscow.

The Soviet atomic power plant had been visited by the scientists who attended the international conference on atomic energy called by the Russians in July, and the visit had been the high spot of that conference, in the opinion of Europeans who had been there. Western scientists found the Russian power reactor very interesting because it used fuel elements of a type different from all others known and assembled of pieces requiring no metallurgical treatment.

Like our own, the Russian exhibit was planned to give a comprehensive idea of the entire field of nuclear energy. Besides the three reactor models and a stand illustrating an automatic control system in a research reactor, the exhibits contained a large array of electronic instruments used both for research and for practical purposes in medicine and industry. Russian equipment looked perhaps less refined than ours in most cases; still it suggested skill and ingenuity. Applications in the industrial field were given more prominence and larger space than in our exhibits. They ranged from a gamma radiation indicator used in well logging to a device to count bottles by interruption of a radiation beam (while a photoelectric device would have sufficed, according to a hypercritical visitor).

In the section on medicine, large pictures of the "before and after the cure" type, occupying the entire length of a wall, showed the success attained by Soviet physicians in the treatment of some forms of cancer of the skin. Russian scientists stressed the fact that statistics could be made on a large number of patients since radioisotopes for medical use were provided free, like all health services in the Soviet Union. Dr. M. N. Fateyeva, a Russian woman scientist, presented a paper by A. V. Kozlova, in which she told how 160 establishments in the Soviet Union had been simultaneously supplied with sets of radioactive preparations in the shape of small tubes and needles. As an example, Dr. Fateyeva said that 450 patients with eyelid skin tumors were treated in one institution alone in Kharkov, with a recovery of 94 per cent of the cases.

A large diagram on a wall illustrated the cycle of carbon nutrition in plants, according to results of original work performed by Russian biologists. It was known that, under the action of light, green plants could fix the carbon dioxide present in the air and form complex substances, like the sugars that furnish the energy needed by animals. It was believed that the carbon dioxide was absorbed by the leaves only. At Geneva the Russians claimed that the role of roots in carbon nutrition had been underestimated. Studying the carbon cycle with radioactive carbon, Kursanov (who gave an evening lecture on the subject) and Kousine found that roots can absorb the carbon dioxide contained in the ground and transmit it to the leaves, where it is utilized, together with the carbon dioxide from the air. The diagram in the exhibits illustrated this theory.

One feature of the Soviet exhibit was unique, *le livre d'or* ("the golden book") for visitors' remarks. Visitors liked the idea of expressing their opinions and used the book freely, signing their statements and giving their addresses. Most of the remarks were laudatory comments by scientists and laymen of almost every country on Soviet progress in nuclear science and technology, and only very few were disparaging. A Swiss publisher offered space in his newspaper to any Russians who wished to write about their work in the nuclear field. One scientist offered a place in his laboratory to the woman mineralogist who had set up the display of uranium minerals and ores, the blond, mannish woman whose daughter was historian at the Kremlin. Most encouraging of the remarks in the golden book were the many expressions of hope that the new science might be used for the good of mankind and not for war, hope summarized in the three words written by an enthusiastic Frenchman, "Vive la paix!"

All that has been said in this chapter about the Russians and their relation with Western scientists goes to prove that the language barriers were overcome to a large degree in one way or another. Still they existed and caused difficulties. One sunny day a group of Russians and Americans were standing in the garden of the Palais des Nations, in front of the Mobile Radiological Unit of the United States Atomic Energy Commission. This unit consisted of a trailer equipped with a complete laboratory for measuring the radioactivity of different types of samples collected in a locality exposed to radiation and for evaluating the health conditions in that locality. The Russians had just been taken through the Radiological Unit and had seen the many instruments in it. They were discussing the electronic devices in the trailer, waving pop bottles which they had just emptied. The Russians wanted to know whether "vacuum lamps or crystal lamps" were used. The meaning of these terms, reaching the Americans through the Russian interpreter, was not understood. Discussions and inquiries went on for some time with the empty bottles vainly attempting to help the verbal expression. It was ascertained in the end that the use of "vacuum tubes" was prevalent in the United States, while in the Soviet Union crystal diodes were preferred. This is one example of what could be a long list of language problems.

Russian scientists made, in general, an excellent impression on their Western colleagues. There is no doubt that scientists on both sides of the Iron Curtain enjoyed their new friendship immensely. Most of our American delegates found the Soviets quite free and willing to answer questions, although this was not always true. Some remarks were made to the effect that it was not easy to obtain information from the Soviets. A few of our scientists had asked specific questions about items on display at the exhibit; the interpreter had been unable to answer them and had called upon the technical personnel in attendance; often not even these had been able to answer and had taken refuge behind the statement that there was a paper on the subject that explained everything in detail. When the relevant paper was delivered, the question was asked again. The speaker then stated that he was not the author of the paper, that he had not worked on the subject, and that he knew little about it. This type of experience seems to have been more frequent in the fields of biology and medicine than in physics, chemistry, or metallurgy.

At our exhibits, in our technical library, and in discussions of all kinds, the Russians were the most eager of all the foreign delegates to obtain detailed information. They took notes, pictures, and measurements in the exhibits; they used the library for serious study. They appeared gratified by any praise of their work and of their exhibit. They gave each delegation a set of reports of their July conference in Moscow, bound in blue leather, and they seemed proud to have such a nice gift to offer.

Political issues had been deliberately excluded from the official program of the conference, and in all their contacts delegates from the East and from the West respected this exclusion. They may have done so unawares or voluntarily; they may have been so engrossed in comparing their work, in talking of topics of common scientific interest, that they had no time to discuss much else; or they may have been afraid to spoil their good relations by bringing controversial issues into their conversations. They shared a great desire to combine their efforts for the advancement of science and the good of mankind, and the rest was unimportant.

9 THE TECHNICAL EXHIBITS

Memorandum to Mr. Gerard C. Smith
State Department
Washington, D.C.

from Mr. John A. Hall
Atomic Energy Commission
Washington

. . . Your assistance is requested in obtaining permission from the Swiss Government to import into Switzerland . . . a small quantity of potato tubers. In addition to the potatoes, we propose to ship to Switzerland around the middle of July the following living plant materials:

Corn Seed	Tobacco Seed
Lettuce Seed	Barley Seed
Soy bean Seed	Pea Seed
Kale Seed	2 dozen bryophillium tubifolium
Wheat Seed	2 dozen carnation plants
Spinach Seed	

We understand from the Department of Agriculture that the Swiss have no restrictions on the import of any of the above plant materials but that a virtual embargo exists on the import of potatoes from the United States, except those from California, due to the danger of Colorado potato beetles. In this case the quantity of potatoes will be very small, each will be wrapped in celophane and we can certify that there will be no danger of transmitting insects of any kind.

This document, found in a filing cabinet of the Atomic Energy Commission, makes one wonder what sort of deals went on in the Commission. The truth is that no one was planning to go into the business of exporting agricultural products. The request for help had come from the Brookhaven National Laboratory in Long Island, where a group of botanists who had studied the effects of radiations on plants wanted to show these effects in living specimens at the conference. They had asked Dr. Seymour Shapiro, one of their group, to assume the responsibility of this part of the exhibit, and he had sought approval of the export of plant material through the proper channels.

Although the Swiss Embassy in Washington had indicated that there should be no difficulty in the shipment of any of the plant material, to be on the safe side it was decided to obtain formal permission from the Swiss government. Accordingly, Mr. Hall's request proceeded through the Department of State and through our Embassy in Switzerland to the Swiss Department of Agriculture, and the answer came back by the same route. The Swiss government handled the request with dispatch, for an affirmative reply was on its way back to the States only ten days after the memorandum had been sent to the Department of State.

So there were no difficulties in sending plant material abroad. But it seemed impossible to take the carnations back to the United States. Import laws barred entrance of foreign soil into this country, and soil that had spent several weeks abroad was foreign for import purposes.

Dr. Shapiro brooded for a while, then he asked an agricultural law expert whether it would be possible to send over soil inclosed in tight plastic bags, to leave the bags at the United States Consulate or at the Embassy, which are legally part of our country, and to use this soil to repot the carnation plants at the last minute before shipping them back. The legal expert saw no objections to this plan, and Dr. Shapiro went ahead with his preparations. Meanwhile he had shipped some seeds to the director of the Swiss Botanical Gardens, Dr. Charles Baehni, who put them in the soil at exactly the right moment to produce little plants in the desired stage of growth at the time of the exhibit.

Why all this fuss? Why rush to Geneva four carnation plants that at the conference did not look particularly attractive after having been kept several days in a refrigerator to preserve the flowers? A farmer visiting the exhibits during the conference remarked that he had seen better-looking carnations on the Riviera! Why not buy seeds to grow wheat, barley, and corn in Switzerland? The answer is that all plant material exhibited at Geneva had been exposed to radiations at Brookhaven.

There were several radiation facilities for botanical research at Brookhaven, the most spectacular of which, from the layman's point of view, was the "gamma field." This was a ten-acre tract of land with a cobalt-60 source of gamma rays in its center. By remote control from outside the fence inclosing the field, the source could either be lowered into a lead container absorbing the radiations or raised to irradiate the field. A simple and ingenious system of locks made it certain that the source could not be raised if any person was inside the field. Plants were arranged in concentric rows around the source so that the closest plants received larger doses of radiation than those farther away, and thus studies on the effects of different doses could be carried on simultaneously.

Both genetic and somatic mutations were produced in this field. Genetic mutations are those occurring in plant gametes. Once a gamete has been affected by radiation, its hereditary composition is changed. When the plant reproduces, the gamete transmits its change to its descendants, and the mutation is carried on generation after generation. Somatic mutations are those occurring in body cells, not in the reproductive ones. A bud, for instance, may be exposed to radiation. One of its cells may undergo mutation and then produce a branch different from the others on the same plant. This different branch can be cut off and grown as a separate plant, and thus the mutation can be propagated asexually. The carnations flown to Geneva had been exposed to gamma radiations in the gamma field and showed somatic mutations: flowers of different colors or single and double flowers bloomed on the same plant.

At Brookhaven, mutations were also produced in seeds. If seeds are exposed to radiation, some of their cells may undergo mutations. When the seeds are grown, some of the mutated cells may become gametes, and in reproducing they will perpetuate the mutation. Experiments at Brookhaven indicated that thermal neutrons are the most effective radiation to produce mutations in seeds. Seeds could be exposed to thermal neutrons in a special cavity of the Brookhaven reactor.

By inducing mutations in seeds it is possible to produce strains of plants with special, useful characteristics, like resistance to some diseases. Thus a rust-resistant strain of oats was obtained: seeds were irradiated and the plants grown from them were exposed to the disease; the few that did not contract it constituted the rust-resistant variety.

Research on the production of useful mutations was carried on at Brookhaven in co-operation with universities, with agricultural experimental stations in the United States and Canada, and with the United States Department of Agriculture. Seeds and other plant material were irradiated at Brookhaven and then returned to the various institutions, which performed their own investigations. The Brookhaven researchers hoped that this co-operative program could be extended to other countries, as the facilities at Brookhaven were adequate to irradiate much larger quantities of seeds and other material than they were doing; so the word was spread at Geneva. As a consequence, Italy sent seeds and cuttings to Brookhaven, and other countries expressed their wish to participate in the co-operative program.

The results of all work in the field of radiation genetics performed at Brookhaven were presented at the Geneva conference. Dr. Willard Ralph Singleton prepared a paper in collaboration with his co-workers, and Dr. Shapiro prepared the exhibit. This included a section of the gamma field with a real source of gamma rays, and real plants growing around it. A thin cobalt wire emitting a weak radiation was sent to Geneva, together with little glass tubes filled with corn kernels, a Geiger counter, pots and trays, and all the other necessary things. Before Dr. Shapiro left Brookhaven for Geneva, he learned that the gamma rays from the cobalt wire, although weak, were not weak enough: if the wire were placed in the exhibits, all the counters on display would start clicking, and all the delicate instruments would soon be out of adjustment. Therefore, when Dr. Shapiro left for Geneva at the end of July, he carried a strange object in his hand, which he hardly ever put down during his trip. It looked like a crumpled, dull roll of tin foil. It was actually a piece of radioactive iridium wire wrapped in lead foil. The iridium wire emitted weaker gamma rays than the cobalt wire, and the lead foil protected Dr. Shapiro's hand from exposure to radiation.

Dr. Shapiro, having been in charge of the co-operative work in the gamma field at Brookhaven for some time, was the logical person to prepare the exhibit. But he was not too eager to do it at first, because it meant taking considerable time from his regular work; besides, some of the unavoidable administrative difficulties delaying his preparations annoyed him. One might have expected to find him grumpy and long-faced at Geneva, but he was not. Dr. Shapiro was a strong, square-faced man with a friendly manner and even disposition who did not mind long hours of work. As soon as he arrived in Geneva, iridium source in hand, he set to work unpacking his fragile glass tubes full of seeds, planting in trays the seedlings grown in the Swiss Botanical Gardens, setting up the wedge of gamma field, and hanging up the large aerial photograph of the field and the colored transparencies showing work on seedlings. His beloved plants needed his care, and he became one of the most assiduous workers at the exhibits. When pictures of each panel were taken at an off time, with no people to hide the view, the photographers could not make Dr. Shapiro part from his exhibit. He stood by it, turning his broad shoulders and the back of his prematurely balding head to the camera, and was the only human being to enliven the cold, lengthy set of exhibit pictures.

In the memorandum quoted at the beginning of this chapter potatoes were mentioned. These had been irradiated with gamma rays to prevent sprouting, thus greatly increasing their storage life. When potatoes were first irradiated, it was not known whether their taste and texture would be altered. To find this out, scientists at Brookhaven were used as guinea pigs. They were fed both irradiated and normal potatoes and were not told which was which; they were not able to tell the difference.

The Brookhaven exhibit was but a tiny part of the United States technical exhibits, and it has here been dealt with in some detail only as an example.

One hundred and seventy-one cases of exhibit components were shipped from New York on June 30, aboard the freighter "American Jurist." Models and components were supplied by industrial organizations, government agencies, and laboratories. Seventy-five cases were shipped to New York on four trucks from Alexandria, Virginia, by Design and Production, Incorporated, the company in charge of planning and assembling the exhibits. More crates arrived from other parts of the country—a considerable number of them, including four reactor models, came from the Argonne National Laboratory near Chicago—and all were loaded on the "American Jurist."

Richard Brecker, who was in charge of supervising the exhibits in

Europe for the OIC, watched the loading of the boat. He saw it pull off with relief. It was gratifying that there was no delay in the shipment, that all or almost all preparations for the exhibits were on schedule. The "American Jurist" was due in Antwerp on July 13, and from there the shipment was to proceed immediately by train to Geneva. Richard Brecker was to arrive in Geneva in time to supervise the setting-up of the displays, and since everything had gone well so far, he was likely to have an easy time. Dr. Alberto Thompson was to reach Geneva not long after Brecker and to assume the over-all responsibility for the exhibits there, as he had in Washington.

But a week later the outlook for the exhibits had changed. On July 7 the port workers at Antwerp called a strike, and the "American Jurist" was diverted to Dunkerque. When this fact became known in Washington, George Weil and Thomas Jones grabbed the telephone, put in transatlantic calls, and dictated telegrams. Through the State Department they asked the assistance of the Belgian Embassy and of the consulates in Geneva and Antwerp.

They learned that facilities at Dunkerque for unloading and forwarding the shipment were poor and were made even worse by the many boats diverted there from Antwerp, that to ship the exhibits by air from Dunkerque was out of the question. On July 14 a cable from Geneva indicated that arrival of the shipment in Geneva might be delayed until as late as July 25. Excitement in Washington reached a peak. Then it was learned that the "American Jurist" would go back to Antwerp and that the United States Consulate there was arranging for volunteers to unload the boat, if the strike continued. The freighter arrived in Antwerp, and the strike was called off on July 16; the exhibit shipment was the first to leave the boat. It was placed on nine railroad cars that were to be unloaded in Geneva at the rate of one a day for nine days; the crates were sorted out in the order in which they would be needed. The strike had caused a delay of two whole days.

Altogether, things were not as simple as they had looked to Dick Brecker. Dr. Thompson became ill, and Brecker was obliged to assume full responsibility for the exhibits, before, during, and after the conference, with the exception of the nine days that Thompson was able to spend in Geneva. Dick Brecker's shoulders were broad enough for the extra burden. Assured and efficient, he went on shuttling between the exhibits at the Palais des Nations and the offices at the Hôtel du Rhône, where he reported directly to George Weil when Alberto Thompson was not there.

When the freight cars with the exhibit components arrived in Geneva, Mr. Shy Greenspan of Design and Production was much relieved, for the deadline was only seventeen days ahead. For several days he had been busy preparing Salle XV in the library wing of the Palais des Nations, helped by an efficient team of Swiss workers. They had rolled up the luxurious rug. The floor under it was plain cement. They had expected marble, and to protect the marble from spilled chemicals and from possible contamination, they were to lay a false wooden floor on top of it. The wooden floor was laid anyway, to distribute the weight of the heavy models and instruments, to leave space for electric cables, and to provide ventilation. Fresh air was drawn through three windows and blown under the floor. The cables went all the way to the basement, where two motor generators transformed the Swiss type of current into the American. They passed through the Soviet exhibit, a fact which caused some concern at first, but which proved quite satisfactory because of the Russians' friendliness.

When the crates arrived from Antwerp, they were lugged up into Salle XV over a ramp and in through a large window. Thus they were not taken through the central hall of the library wing, and the people studying in the library were not disturbed by the noise. The empty crates were stored away, to be used again for the return trip.

The exhibits were set up according to a logical plan. If you want to produce atomic energy, you must start by getting the essential raw materials: uranium and thorium to use as fuel, beryllium and graphite to slow down and reflect neutrons, aluminum to clad fuel elements and for structural parts, zirconium to replace aluminum in reactors where great corrosion is expected. So the first section of the exhibits illustrated materials and their properties. The next section contained fuel elements; then came the reactor models, which occupied about one-third of the entire exhibition. Besides reactor models, the reactor display included a reactor control panel, control mechanisms, instruments, and reactor parts. After a display of a chemical processing plant and of a hot laboratory to handle highly radioactive samples, there was a section containing instruments for prospecting, for monitoring, for medical and scientific use. The last part of the exhibits illustrated the applications of radioisotopes in industry, medicine, and biology. All captions were in the four official languages. An exhibit brochure, also in the four languages, was distributed to all visitors wishing it.

The United States technical exhibits were visited by 36,200 persons. The delegates of the various countries were the visitors who showed the most serious interest. They wanted to *learn* from the exhibits: they spent hours and hours, stopping in front of each case, each model, each shelf. They listened to the explanations given by the Ph.D.'s on duty; they asked questions, took notes and pictures. The Russian delegates, who were the most assiduous of all, came back with their cameras time after time. Before taking a picture, they always asked permission, although they were repeatedly told that they could photograph the exhibits whenever they wished. They also asked to take moving pictures, and it was arranged that they do so at night, when they would not disturb the public or themselves be disturbed by it.

The general public was by and large less appreciative. They looked at the exhibits out of curiosity, but seldom did they try to understand what they saw. "The exhibits," a Ph.D. later had occasion to comment, "were above the public's head." There were exceptions. Many non-delegate European engineers asked questions "which it was a pleasure to answer." A young boy, fascinated by the large number of knobs on the instruments, turned them all, and before the puzzled scientists could understand what was happening, all instruments were out of adjustment. The boy was found hiding behind a large reactor model.

The reader, whose interest is probably halfway between that of the delegates and that of the uninterested public, will not receive the exhaustive guided tour that only a Ph.D. in science could give, but he will be taken for a visit to Salle XV and asked to stop only here and there to get some idea of what the exhibits were like. He will also see what a small part of the whole exhibit the Brookhaven display of Radiations and Plant Genetics was. He will then realize what a large number of people worked on the exhibits as hard as, or perhaps even harder than, Dr. Shapiro, and how many interesting stories they might tell about their work, which are not told here only for lack of space.

The tour starts at the entrance of Salle XV, where an old Swiss guard in a blue uniform made certain that only delegates went inside during the hours reserved for delegates. He stood, tall and thin, leaning now and then against the door jamb to rest his shoulders, which were rounded with age. Once, toward the end of the conference, he was asked how he had liked his task. "It is a little tiring at my age to be standing on my feet eight hours a day," he answered quietly, without moving at all, his long bony hands pressed against his legs. "But it is interesting. Yes, I have seen people of all races except Eskimos."

Outside the door, well in sight of the Swiss guard, there was a huge box, four by eight feet in size, which attracted the attention of many people. It was a continuous cloud chamber. A cloud chamber makes it possible to see the tracks of ionizing radiations. The chamber is filled with a supersaturated vapor, usually alcohol vapor. Supersaturated vapors tend to condense around any small particle, be it an impurity, a speck of dust, or an ion, which is a positively charged corpuscle. It is this tendency that causes the formation of fog and clouds.

An ionizing particle traveling in the chamber hits the atoms in its path, pulls electrons from them, and thus originates ions. The supersaturated vapor filling the chamber condenses around these ions in threads of fog. A strong beam of light may make them appear luminous and bright. Thus the path of the particle is revealed.

The cloud chamber at the exhibits showed at any one moment a very large number of tracks, about five hundred of them. Yet no radioactive substance was placed inside the chamber or near it. The tracks were due to the swarm of ionizing particles which normally fill the air as background radiation because of the cosmic rays and radon normally in the atmosphere. All life has evolved in the presence of this radiation, which, according to the geneticists, is responsible for part of the spontaneous mutations always occurring in living organisms.

Entering the room, the visitor faced the reception desk and the two attractive girls behind it. The desk functioned as an information booth for the United States delegation: messages were left there; journalists came to make appointments for picture-taking and for interviews with scientists; the public came to ask directions. The girls, who could among them speak the four official languages, tried to answer all questions.

They had one hard time when a woman came to buy uranium to heat her home. She had read in the local paper that the United States was selling natural uranium at forty dollars per kilogram, and, after a little figuring, she had come to the conclusion that it was quite inexpensive. The girls at the desk tried to explain that uranium could not be used like coal, by just placing it in a furnace; special devices were needed and those were quite expensive. "But you don't know," the woman insisted, "how high my heating bill runs!"

Admiral Strauss announced the sale price of uranium on August 8, the first day of the conference, together with the price of heavy water: twenty-eight dollars per pound—the Norwegians, who had been the main heavy water producers up to then, were selling it at a much higher price and were said to be unhappy about the United States price. Mr. Strauss also announced the lease value of uranium enriched to 20 per cent of U-235—twenty-five dollars per gram of contained U-235.

To the right of the receiving desk was the display "Production of Uranium and Thorium Metals." Mineral samples of surprisingly pretty colors were displayed in two glass showcases: there was a uranium mineral, called gummite, yellow with green pigments and orange veins; others were all bright green or bright orange; a uranium silicate from South Dakota, called coffinite, was as black as salt is white. A card by each sample indicated not only the mineral's chemical composition but also the place where it was mined.

Not far from the mineral cases was the display of fuel elements. These had given Mr. Greenspan quite a headache during the preparations for the exhibit. Fourteen fuel elements were to be displayed by the United States in Geneva, but when Shy Greenspan had started to plan the exhibits in Virginia he was shown only a few of the elements, since the others were still classified at that time. He had asked Mr. William Young and Mr. Robert Butenhoff of the Atomic Energy Commission, who were assisting him, to give him some information on the classified elements: What would they look like? How much wall space would they take? How heavy would they be? "Oh," said the scientists vaguely, "give them the same consideration you have given to the ones you saw. You cannot go far wrong." The fuel elements proved to be the prize pieces of our technical exhibits. No other country displayed them or described their fabrication. They attracted many scientists with cameras, measuring tapes, and notebooks, and Russian delegates more than any others. All fuel elements were shining, elongated objects of elegant design: sets of plates or rods, winged tubes, long cylinders. In the exhibit they were arranged according to the substance with which they were clad— aluminum, zirconium, or stainless steel.

After the fuel elements came the reactor models. These also had caused trouble for Greenspan. All his life he had dealt with art— first he had studied it for fourteen years and since then he had been selling other people's art. He knew nothing of science or scientific terminology. Young and Butenhoff were very considerate and wanted to explain everything to him, but in their own language. They told him that the Argonne National Laboratory would take care of the CP-5, EBWR, and EBR models and that Phillips Petroleum Company would ship MTR directly to New York. At first Greenspan could not make out what the scientists were talking about. But he soon guessed that the initials represented names of particular reactors and asked the two scientists to *please* avoid short cuts for a while, until he had memorized that CP stood for "Chicago Pile," and MTR stood for "Material Testing Reactor," and that an E appearing anywhere, in any combination of initials, meant "Experimental."

The first five reactor models in the display illustrated the United States experimental reactor program, which was undertaken in 1954 as a five-year program. Out of the large number of possible reactor designs, perhaps eighty or more, the Atomic Energy Commission had selected and recommended for construction five types that had been extensively explored for several years and that appeared the most likely to lead to competitive atomic power. Their development was sponsored by the government with a view to studying different technical approaches to practical nuclear power and to obtaining information on costs of construction and operation. Four of the five reactors were under construction at the time of the Geneva conference. One of these, the Shippingport Pressurized Water Reactor (PWR) was to be the first full-scale nuclear power plant for civilian use in the United States and was to produce 60,000 kilowatts.

The plant at Shippingport, near Pittsburgh in Pennsylvania, to be operated by the Duquesne Light Company, which had undertaken the construction of the turbogenerator, was designed for completion in 1957. The main part of the plant—the reactor—was being constructed by Westinghouse Electric Corporation. The model at the exhibit showed the entire plant: the reactor was cooled and moderated by ordinary water under a pressure of two thousand pounds per square inch to prevent it from boiling. The water brought the heat developed by the reactor to four heat exchangers, or steam generators. The steam operated the turbine. The fuel consisted of highly enriched fuel elements surrounded by a blanket of natural uranium.

A plant this size, though not large enough to achieve maximum economy for this reactor design, was sufficient to provide operating experience. Plants of this type could be built in foreign countries sooner than other types, and with relatively minor redesigning they could operate on natural uranium, if heavy water was used instead of natural water. In recommending the construction of this plant, the Joint Congressional Committee on Atomic Energy had stated: "As a demonstration of the serious intent of the United States to develop peacetime uses of atomic energy for both ourselves and our allies . . . construction of one large-scale plant such as the pressurized water reactor is important."

The second model in the display was that of the Experimental Boiling Water Reactor (EBWR), a small plant under construction at the Argonne National Laboratory, scheduled for completion in 1956 and designed to produce five thousand kilowatts of electricity. Like other reactor models prepared at Argonne, this also was complete with service buildings and landscaping—green bushes and trees—and was inclosed in a round plastic dome, perfectly transparent, through which one could see every single detail. The reactor used slightly enriched uranium and was moderated and cooled by water that was allowed to boil and produce steam. The steam went directly to the turbine, a great simplification over most designs, which needed heat exchangers and additional pumps. The transparent dome was misleading: it would have been a disappointment to visit the construction site at the Argonne National Laboratory after the Geneva conference and to stand in front of a tall dome of dull steel through which absolutely nothing of the inside could be seen. Domes inclosing reactor plants are designed to provide safety to the population around them: in case of an accident the radio-activity produced would be contained inside the dome.

The next model, also built at the Argonne National Laboratory, also enlivened by bushes and trees and showing its interior perfectly through transparent walls, was the model of the Experimental Breeder Reactor No. 2 (EBR). Its construction, due for completion in 1958, had not started at the time of the Geneva conference. This reactor was called "No. 2" because of a previous breeder reactor, which had demonstrated on a small scale that more fissionable material can be produced than is consumed. The model of EBR showed a fast reactor, in which fast neutrons, rather than slowed-down neutrons, produced fission; hence the reactor had no moderator. Its core was of highly enriched uranium surrounded by a blanket of uranium 238. The coolant was liquid metal sodium. Liquid metal sodium becomes highly radioactive and also reacts violently if it comes in contact with water, adding to the difficulties of designing and constructing this type of reactor.

The fourth model, that of the Homogeneous Reactor Experiment (HRE) under construction at Oak Ridge National Laboratory, was a glass box filled with a very intricate system of tubes, most of them made of glass, some of metal. The reason for so many tubes was that a Homogeneous Reactor does not use solid fuel but a water solution of highly enriched uranyl sulfate. Among the advantages of homogeneous reactors are the facts that they are self-regulating and need no control rods; that there are no fuel elements to be fabricated and reprocessed; that fuel recycling is easier. The main disadvantages come from the uranium salt solution circulating in pumps and heat exchangers, which is very radioactive and corrosive.

The model of the Homogeneous Reactor was shipped from Oak Ridge; to avoid breakage of the many tubes inside the glass box, it had been stuffed with popcorn, which is said to have excellent anti-shock properties. The Swiss workers at the exhibits had never seen popcorn. Having tasted and liked it, they put it into bags and took it home to their families.

The fifth and last reactor model in the government's five-year program display was that of the Sodium Reactor Experiment (SRE), developed by North American Aviation, Incorporated, in California. This reactor was designed to use graphite as moderator and liquid sodium as coolant. This coolant permitted the attainment of high temperature and high steam pressure, and consequently of greater thermal efficiency than other systems. On the other hand, the radioactivity and corrosiveness of sodium constituted great difficulties.

The reader will be spared a few other reactor models and the drawings of larger power plants proposed by industries and under study by the government. One more model, that of the Material Testing Reactor (MTR), cannot be overlooked because it was so large that it dominated the entire reactor section of the exhibits. There is a better reason for mentioning this reactor: it preceded all those described above and facilitated their design and construction. Completed in 1952 at the National Reactor Testing Station in Idaho and operated by the Phillips Petroleum Company, it was aimed primarily at obtaining information about the effects of radiation on fuel elements and on structural materials and at determining fundamental constants for reactor development.

In line with its purpose, the reactor was provided with many experimental facilities, among which was a thermal column on one side, six feet square and eight feet long. The main part of the reactor, as its model showed, rose four stories above ground and went at least two stories underground. The central part of the model, containing the control mechanisms and the fuel elements, was much taller than the rest and almost reached the ceiling of Salle XV, yet the little men placed on the stairways and on the top platform were no more than six or seven inches tall.

For scientifically minded visitors and delegates one of the most interesting exhibits was a working pilot plant that could separate and purify uranium. Scientists from Oak Ridge were at hand to operate the plant and explain the ion-exchange method used in it, which is based on the ability of some resins to form negative ions and to retain uranium but not other metals. The general public found the explanations difficult, the chemistry uninteresting, and walked by the pilot plant without stopping.

They stopped a few paces away, though, in front of the hot cell where the highly radioactive solutions from the separation plant could be analyzed at a distance with manipulators, or magic hands— the same ones that had changed the mood of the first Russian visitors. The magic hands drew a broad grin from Admiral Strauss, who operated them under the eyes of television cameras. A few days before, he had asked to operate a similar set on display in the popular exhibit of the United States Information Agency in the Palais des Expositions; but the pretty girl in charge of the manipulators was under strict orders and refused permission.

The manipulators consisted of two sets of long shiny metal tubes coming down from the ceiling outside the walls of the hot cell and connected to two tubes on the inside. The tubes on the outside ended with three rings for the first three fingers of the operator's hand. Each of the tubes inside terminated in a piece that looked like the beak of a strong bird of prey. It opened and closed, moved forward and backward, upward and downward, in extraordinary co-ordination with the operator's motions. The operator could perform an analysis watching the beak-like ends of the manipulators through a three-foot-thick window.

A little farther on, in the instrument section, the visitor would see one or another of the scientists who had come from the Los Alamos Scientific Laboratory to deliver papers at the conference, standing by a slender, gray cabinet as tall as a man. It was a one-hundred-channel pulse-height analyzer, built at Los Alamos, and the scientists were eager to explain its extraordinary features to all willing to listen. It could analyze radiations, give a visible description of them, and store information about them for later use, the scientists said. It worked in connection with a radiation detector: as radioactive substances disintegrate they emit radiations the energy of which is characteristic for each substance. A radioactive compound could be placed in the analyzer. The detector then produced an electrical pulse at each disintegration, and the height of the pulse was proportional to the energy of the radiation emitted. The analyzer sorted the various pulses into one hundred pigeonholes, each corresponding to an equal interval of energy.

It could show this information in the form of a luminous graph on a built-in oscilloscope. An observer could see at a glance the number of pulses in each of the hundred intervals, and so he could look for pulses characteristic of a special substance and thus detect this substance even if present in small amounts. Pictures could be taken of this graph and studied at leisure. If the information was not needed at once, it could be stored in the magnetic memory, which was similar to that used in modern computing machines. It was made of two thousand tiny magnetic cores and was able to store up to one hundred numbers, each of which could be as large as 99,999. The number of pulses stored in each channel could be tabulated and added as desired, automatically and rapidly.

The analyzer's memory was tougher than that of human beings. Could the reader imagine a human brain taken apart, then put together again, and still able to remember the events of weeks earlier? This is exactly what happened to the pulse-height analyzer: in Los Alamos some radioactive material was placed in it and the instrument analyzed it and told the results. The information was also stored in its memory. Then the instrument was taken apart, the pieces placed in boxes and sent to Geneva; there it was reassembled. As soon as electric current of the American type became available at the exhibits, the analyzer was asked to tell once more the figures relative to the substance analyzed in Los Alamos. They were exactly the same.

The first hundred-channel pulse-height analyzer was built in Los Alamos in 1954 and placed in service early in 1955. It was then decided to build two more. Construction began in February, 1955, about the time scientists in Los Alamos had started thinking of their possible contributions to the conference. They considered sending one of the new analyzers to Geneva. In the end they sent both, since the one could make a complete set of spares for the other and save worries and expenses for maintenance. The shipment from Los Alamos, twenty-eight boxes weighing thirty-two hundred pounds, went from nearby Albuquerque to Geneva via Trans World Airlines and suffered no damage, as proved by the memory test. The memory of the second analyzer was displayed separately and was left open to show its complicated inner construction.

The Los Alamos scientists who were in Geneva were pleased with their elaborate display and spent some time taking care of it and showing it to the visitors. One day the young man on duty at the analyzer saw Mr. Greenspan approaching with a heavy-set, white-haired man who walked slowly, his head bent forward, his bushy eyebrows almost brushing his high cheeks. At Shy Greenspan's request the young man started to explain the analyzer to the older man. Uncertain of how technical he should be, the scientist asked,

"Do you know any electronics?" "A little," the older man answered with a twinkle in his soft blue eyes. "I forgot to introduce Professor Niels Bohr from Denmark!" exclaimed Mr. Greenspan. Such is the reputation of Professor Bohr, the father of all modern theories on the atoms, that the young man from Los Alamos was left speechless for a moment and then barely managed to pursue his explanations. Mr. Greenspan was accompanying Professor Bohr on a tour of the exhibits. "All he said was 'Very nice! It is very nice,' " Mr. Greenspan recounted later with a bit of wonder. Anyone can say "Very nice," but of great men unusual sayings are expected, for it is forgotten that they are like anyone else in most ways and can make the same remarks.

The reader who is getting tired of the exhibits, although he has missed many of them, will be pleased to know that he has already walked along more than three of the four corridors into which Salle XV was divided by that part of the display set up in its center. The entrance was near one end of one of the two long corridors, and the reader is now standing at the other end. In this last stretch he will find the applications of radioisotopes, mostly in the fields of biology and medicine, some in industry.

The most important use that radioisotopes have found in medical therapy is the treatment of some forms of cancer. Broadly speaking, there are two main methods of treating cancer with radiation: by teletherapy and by implantation of radioisotopes inside the body. This second method is called "brachytherapy." Both methods were illustrated in the exhibits. In the brachytherapy panel there were photographs showing results of treatment, sources of various shapes and sizes, and instruments to implant and remove the sources. Seven models of teletherapy units used or under construction in the United States were displayed. The units contained a source of high energy radiation, such as radioactive cobalt, cesium, and iridium; a strong beam of radiation could be released through a small opening and directed with great precision on the patient.

A third method of treating cancer with radiations, still under study at the time of the conference, was illustrated at the exhibits with photographs and drawings: the slow neutron capture therapy of brain tumors. This method of treatment was developed by Dr. Lee Farr and collaborators at Brookhaven National Laboratory, and was described at the conference in a paper read by Dr. Farr. It is based on a novel and imaginative idea: that radioactivity can be induced inside a brain tumor, as needed, by the action of slow neutrons.

To achieve this, it is necessary that a suitable substance be made to concentrate in the tumor. This substance must become active when hit by slow neutrons and emit heavy particles capable of traveling only very short distances, thus destroying the tumor cells on their path without harming the surrounding tissues. Boron fulfils this qualification: it can capture slow neutrons and subsequently decay, emitting alpha particles, which are heavy and short-ranged.

Boron can be made to concentrate temporarily in a brain tumor: normal brain tissues possess a "barrier" that prevents substances in the blood from diffusing rapidly in the tissues. Tumors, however, do not have this barrier. Boron, if injected in the blood, will enter the brain tumor much faster than the other tissues of the brain. Thus, for a certain interval of time, the concentration of boron is much greater in the tumor than in the surrounding tissues.

Dr. Farr based his treatment on these facts. In practice, the patient to be treated would first receive an injection of boron; while the boron concentration was higher in the tumor than in the surrounding tissues, he would be made to lie on top of the reactor, with his head carefully placed over a small hole in the shielding, from which an intense beam of slow neutrons emerged. Dr. Farr hoped that the alpha particles emitted by the boron atoms in the tumor, under the action of the slow neutrons, would destroy the tumor and thus cure the patient.

Only nineteen patients had been treated by the slow neutron capture therapy before the Geneva conference, but the results were judged sufficiently encouraging to justify the designing of a special reactor to be built at Brookhaven for medical purposes.

The panel illustrating the slow neutron capture therapy was very close to Dr. Shapiro's previously described display of radiations and plant genetics, and the visitor could not fail to see him. Not far from his exhibit there was another botanical display, at which the visitor will make his last stop before leaving Salle XV. This exhibit, called "Carbon-14 Biosynthesis," described work done at the Argonne National Laboratory and included a tiny greenhouse containing living plants. The tiny greenhouse was a scale model of the sealed glass chambers constructed at Argonne to grow plants in an atmosphere enriched with radioactive carbon-14 in the form of carbon dioxide. By the process of photosynthesis, green plants are able to combine carbon dioxide with water and food elements, utilizing energy supplied by sunlight, to form their normal carbon-containing products. The products manufactured by plants grown in the Argonne chambers contained radioactive carbon; thus, among other products, radioactive tobacco, rubber, opium, and alfalfa were obtained and could be used to produce other radioactive substances that could not be made in the laboratory. The pancreas of mammals fed with radioactive alfalfa, for instance, could yield radioactive insulin for medical studies of diabetes. From cabbages and tomatoes grown in the carbon-14 chambers radioactive vitamin C was extracted, which could be used in tracer studies of rheumatic fever. Radioactive products obtained at Argonne were on display in Geneva near the model of the greenhouse, together with exhaustive explanatory captions.

The tour of Salle XV is now completed and only a few words remain to be said. After the closing of the conference the exhibits were dismantled, each item repacked in its crate and shipped back to the United States on the freighter "American Attorney." The exhibits were set up again in New York from October 20 to November 3, under the sponsorship of the Atomic Industrial Forum, the Carnegie Endowment for International Peace, and the Fund for Peaceful Atomic Development. The two one-hundred-channel pulse-height analyzers did not go to New York, but were flown directly to Los Alamos, where they were put into use at once.

The United States Technical Library was set up in the Salle Chinoise, a room of moderate size, near Salle XV. The library staff was the only group of the United States mission to Geneva that had an equal number of men and women: three men and three women.

The men, Dr. Frank Owings, Mr. Bernard M. Fry, and Mr. Martens of the Atomic Energy Commission's Technical Information Service, were responsible for setting up the library and for its operation. The three women were librarians and among them mastered the four official languages, for, besides English, each spoke at least one other: Simone Schwind, who had come from Oak Ridge, conversed often in French with visitors, with no apparent difficulty or hesitation; Rita Martinez of Los Alamos was the expert in Spanish; and Rita Liepina of the Library of Congress in Washington was in the enviable position of being able to understand what the Russians said. This ability caused her to receive several requests during the two weeks of the conference to attend parties or ceremonies at which Russians were expected. So, the three librarians could answer the queries of the many visitors without the help of interpreters.

Perhaps the most assiduous and studious of the delegates, the librarians remarked, were the Russians. They asked assistance in finding the information they were looking for, then settled at one of the tables and became so engrossed in their profound research that they were lost to the world. The material at their disposal covered the field of the peaceful atom. It comprised one set of the depository library, which the United States Atomic Energy Commission had made available to friendly nations who wanted it, and commercially published books on atomic energy and journals containing articles on it. A map on the wall showed the thirty countries that had already received a depository library: none was behind the Iron Curtain, a fact that may help explain the interest of the Russians. Now that the United States collection was at hand, they took liberal advantage of it. Eager as they always appeared to return any kindness received in Geneva, they made a gift to the library of several sets of their papers for the conference, of two sets of the attractive, blue leather-bound proceedings of the Moscow conference in July, and of several Russian technical books.

Although one depository library in a country was better than none, it was not always sufficient to provide easily accessible information to all interested in it. An Australian felt that, although Australia had one such library, the firm for which he was working ought to buy another for the use of its people, and he asked the librarians whether this would be possible. The answer was that any request of the kind should go through regular diplomatic channels.

A large number of the technical reports contained in the United States collection were not available in full size but were set on microcards. These and the two microcard viewers aroused the interest of many visitors. A man from the Union Minière du Haut-Katanga in the Belgian Congo grew especially lyrical about them. The method was splendid, really remarkable—he was going to set up something of the sort—perhaps it would be less expensive to order the cards rather than try to make them. It might cost a little more, *mais ça serait l'idéal* ("it would be the ideal way").

A man interested in the legislative aspect of the atomic energy took along his secretary and spent much time copying all relevant articles from current laws. Delegates of those countries in which atomic programs were not yet developed asked mostly for literature on the applications of isotopes in medicine, because medicine touches directly all human beings and so the medical uses of the atom interest them the most.

In the technical library at Geneva, besides the reference material, there was limited literature for distribution to delegates: some technical reprints, descriptions and instructions for the use of the depository libraries, price lists of publications for sale in the United States, and descriptions, prepared by commercial firms, of items on display in the technical exhibit and reactor chalet (the OIC did not allow commercial literature as such to be distributed in either place). It was a feature of the conference that the free booklets, pamphlets, leaflets, and press releases distributed anywhere in Geneva, went as fast as hot cakes. Visitors left the grounds of the Palais des Nations with bundles of printed matter under their arms. If later put to proper use, those bundles may have done much to disseminate valuable information on the peaceful atom.

Another function of the library was to distribute the sets of selected reference material to the official representatives of all nations attending the conference. Admiral Strauss had written a letter to the chiefs of delegations announcing that this gift was in the library, ready for their representatives. The boxed, eight-volume sets were attractively displayed: their final position on the shelves had been arrived at through consultations between Goerge Weil and the librarians, and through several trials at making them look their best (inside their box or outside; a few in and a few out, etc.). They were dear to George Weil, and he handled them personally during these trials, while he let the library staff arrange all other publications as they wished. They had planned to hand out only the introductory volume directly to the representatives and to ask them where they wished to have the other volumes shipped. The introductory volume, with its brief description of the content of the other volumes and with the beautiful colored pictures, would give the representatives an idea of what they would get later, once back home. But some of them, perhaps not trusting mail services, insisted on taking along the heavy box containing all eight volumes when they left the library.

The dedication for the introductory volume was written by President Eisenhower on May 3, 1955. It was reprinted on placards and displayed both at the technical exhibit and in the reactor chalet. It said:

The atom cannot be limited by national boundaries.

Men of science from many countries, often working together, help to harness its great energy for the good of mankind. The Geneva Conference on Peaceful Uses of Atomic Energy is a tribute to the inventive genius of these men. At the same time, it demonstrates to people everywhere that continued international cooperation is essential if we are to realize man's capacity to create for himself an increasingly productive world, living at peace.

The great strides already made in putting atomic energy to work in industry, agriculture, medicine and research, will become evident during the course of this Conference. We hope that the free exchange of technical information and ideas among leading scientists and engineers of many nations will stimulate even greater progress in the months and years ahead.

In this cause, the United States is firmly dedicated to promote international cooperation and to contribute its share of scientific knowledge and resources.

The introductory volume also contained a preface by Chairman Strauss, which was repeated in each of the eight volumes of the set. It stated in part:

The purpose of this collection is to provide information concerning the ways that we have found in which fissionable materials can be put to work in nuclear reactors for research purposes and for the production of radioisotopes.

It is our sincere hope that this material will be of practical value to the men and women of science and engineering in whose hands the great power of the atom is becoming a benign force for world peace.

On August 20, Commissioner Libby, acting on behalf of the United States government, presented the technical library to the United Nations, in a radio-broadcast ceremony in which Chief Librarian A. C. Breycha Vauthier received the gift for the United Nations. Dr. Libby delivered a brief speech, giving assurance that the United States Atomic Energy Commission would keep the depository library up to date and would send to it, as indeed it sent to all other depository libraries in the world, future non-classified reports.

When the library exhibit was finally closed to the public on August 21, over nineteen thousand people had visited it. At other exhibits a guard on duty had kept a little counter in his hand, clicking it each time a person came in. The counter had furnished the record of the attendance. But no counter was provided for the library, and the six members of the staff had taken turns watching the doors and tallying the number of visitors on a sheet of paper.

The Mobile Radiological Unit, already mentioned in chapter 8, had a larger attendance—twenty-five thousand people—perhaps because it was stationed outdoors on the pleasant grounds of the Palais des Nations, where delegates liked to wander after long hours inside the lecture halls. The Radiological Unit was built by the Health and Safety Laboratory of the Division of Biology and Medicine of the Atomic Energy Commission and could perform all sorts of tests in zones near laboratories and industrial establishments where radioactivity was handled. It was designed so that the instruments inside it could be changed according to specific needs. In the United Nations gardens it was placed at a square angle to a Swedish ambulance designed for much the same purpose, according to a Swedish leaflet—namely, for "investigation of normal and abnormal radioactivity in the air, water and solid samples. Measurements of contaminated objects including human beings. Search for lost radioactive preparations and investigations for the prevention of damage due to radioactivity spread by accident or otherwise."

10 POWER

To the pure scientists whose main goal is the acquisition of knowledge the challenge of atomic energy lies in its power as a tool of research. With this tool, so much sharper and more refined than any previously available, they hope to speed up the process of learning and to gain a much deeper understanding of nature than has so far been possible to attain. But pure scientists are always a small minority among their fellow men, and so they were even at the Geneva conference. The observers and most of the delegates were mainly interested in what they considered the practical side of atomic science: the production of nuclear power. Our civilization is based on power and on the belief that there is no limit to progress provided enough power is at hand. A speaker at the conference said in his paper, "Any imaginative discussion of prospective uses of atomic energy exposes a multitude of possibilities. If we explore other planets in atomic-powered space ships or descend into the oceans' depths with a future Captain Nemo in his atomic-powered submarine, there is no telling what we may not discover that is relevant to our inquiry." Most people's dreams did not reach this far; still atomic power had struck the fancy of all.

The general interest in power production was reflected in the program of the conference, which devoted a considerable time to one aspect or another of this topic. The new atomic technology was presented in detail at reactor sessions, and at chemistry, metallurgy, and technology sessions. But, even before these started, the main broad aspects of widespread utilization of atomic energy for power were discussed and a number of facts were brought to light at the general sessions during the first three days of the conference.

It was then learned that the generation of electricity with nuclear energy not only was possible but had been achieved and continued steadily for some time in several small power plants, one in the Soviet Union, the others in the United States. Several countries were building full-scale plants from which they expected to gain operating experience and to gather data on costs, but none had yet been completed. The designs of the various plants were different. In each a nuclear reactor took the place of the boiler in a thermal power station, and the heat developed by fission in the nuclear fuel was utilized to produce steam, which was made to move a turbogenerator. The type of the reactor varied. A large number of different reactors for production of power had been designed; several were built on an experimental basis, in a small size, and tested. While each type showed some attractive features, none so far had proved unquestionably superior to others in all respects.

The relative cost of electricity generated in nuclear power plants and in conventional plants appeared to be the most important factor influencing the widespread use of nuclear energy for the production of electricity. The cost of nuclear power was not expected to be cheaper than power from coal for some time, at least in industrially developed countries. Yet optimism prevailed. In time the reserves of coal and oil would decrease, the demands for power would likely increase, and so would the price of electricity produced in plants other than atomic. At the same time, with development of technology and large-scale production, the price of nuclear power was likely to go down substantially. It was stated that in some less-developed zones of the world nuclear power might be competitive even at current prices. Uranium is an enormously more concentrated fuel than coal and thus much more easily and cheaply transported. It appeared possible that nuclear power plants might help develop isolated areas even without the building of costly railroad systems. Some mining districts, for instance in South Africa, in Canada, and in Australia, are remote from oil and coal, and the power they use is several times more expensive than elsewhere. There nuclear power might be economical.

Atomic experts made it clear that in predicting the future of nuclear power they had to do a lot of what the Americans called "speculating" and the British "crystal-gazing," for they did not have the answers to many technical and economic questions. What was the life-expectancy of a reactor? How fast would better reactors be designed and how obsolete would this make those already built? How frequently would fuel elements need to be reprocessed? How far would they have to be shipped for reprocessing? Reprocessing plants were likely to be always very expensive; how many reactors would it be possible to service with one such plant? How much valuable fissionable material could be regenerated as a by-product— plutonium from uranium 238 and uranium 233 from thorium? And what would be the value of by-products? What insurance premiums would be set on nuclear plants? Until these questions and many others were answered in the light of actual experience, no accurate estimates could be made.

One of the reasons for developing several reactor designs at the same time was to determine which had inherent characteristics of safety and could therefore reduce to the minimum the hazards of a nuclear plant. Reactors were potentially dangerous because they contained large amounts of radioactivity—the more powerful the reactor, the larger the amount of radioactivity. Under certain unusual circumstances some of the radioactivity could leak out and contaminate the surrounding areas. One of the possible reactor accidents was a "runaway": it was conceivable that the chain reaction might get out of control, that a very high power might be reached in an exceedingly short time with enormous production of heat. The reactor might then explode, or its components might melt; in both cases its structure would be so disrupted that much radioactivity could escape. Apart from accidents, nuclear plants under normal operation would produce radioactive wastes in large quantities, and their disposal constituted another hazard.

In the evaluation of hazards two main schools of thought could be discerned at the conference. Most of the old "reactor men" considered nuclear reactors safe. They stated that a runaway was very unlikely, that a good system of automatic controls could prevent it, and furthermore that reactors could be designed in such a way that a sudden increase in power and heat would tend to reduce the power and to shut the reactor down; that in any case, even in the remote eventuality that a reactor were to run away, the resulting explosion would be mild; that if the reactor were inclosed in a gas-tight building or in a metal sphere the population would be sufficiently protected even from an explosion.

The opinions of the other school of thought were expressed by Dr. C. Rogers McCullough, Chairman of the United States Advisory Committee on Reactor Safety. Dr. McCullough was professionally cautious. He realized that in the major establishments in all countries adequate safety precautions to prevent accidents were taken. Yet, he had been "specifically requested to look at hazard problems." This he did, and thoroughly. He agreed that "a nuclear reactor would not run away unless a number of serious mistakes of planning and operating were to be committed." But he also stated that "there is still no fool-proof system. Any system can be defeated by a great enough fool." He made it his business to determine and point out the ways in which things might go wrong. In all types of accidents, he concluded, there would be escape of radioactivity from the reactor. If radioactivity were to escape from the reactor building, it might "be carried in the wind and spread over adjacent populated areas and constitute an acute hazard." In his paper he made specific recommendations for designs for safe reactors and reactor buildings and ended by expressing the hope that no dire event would delay the benefits from reactor development.

While costs and safety characteristics of reactors were being investigated, the governments of some countries, such as Great Britain and the United States, were asking industry to participate in their power-development programs, and business to invest capital in them. No wonder that interest in Geneva should center on nuclear power and that everyone should want to hear how the first power plants had performed so far! The Assembly Hall was crowded for the general session at which two papers describing the first power plants were delivered, one after the other: "The First Atomic Power Station in the USSR and the Prospects of Atomic Production" was delivered by the Russian Professor Blokhintsev; "Design and Operating Experience of a Prototype Boiling Water Power Reactor" was presented by Dr. Walter Zinn, Director of the Argonne National Laboratory. Both these papers were allowed forty-five minutes for oral presentation, a longer time than that allotted to any other of the 450 papers presented at Geneva. That morning Sir John Cockcroft was session chairman. To match the solemnity of the occasion, Professor Blokhintsev had donned a silk-lapeled black morning coat. In the Western, more informal, fashion Dr. Zinn wore a blue suit.

Professor Blokhintsev described the plant producing five thousand kilowatts of electricity whose model was in the Russian technical exhibit; he showed slides of pictures that appeared also in the film

"First in the World" shown at the exhibit and at the cinema of the Palais des Nations. A description of the plant was given in the chapter on Russian scientists and will not be repeated here. Professor Blokhintsev said that the Russian power station was built "to accumulate technical and economic experience . . . and to serve as a base to train personnel." It had proved extremely safe and reliable. No overexposure of personnel had occurred and no "harmful influence of the work of the station on the health of the workers was observed." "The cost of one kilowatt hour of electric energy produced by the first atomic power station exceeds considerably the average cost of one kilowatt hour in powerful heat power stations in the USSR. . . . However . . . [it] is comparable in cost with that of a similar type low-power thermal power station." Costs would probably drop, said Professor Blokhintsev, when fuel elements were fabricated in larger numbers; also, with larger reactors the fuel enrichment could be lowered: in the first power station, uranium enriched to 5 per cent of U-235 was used, while in larger reactors a 2.5 per cent enrichment would be sufficient; the conversion ratio of U-238 into plutonium could be increased to provide more of a valuable by-product. Future plants would not necessarily follow the pattern set by the first, and water-moderated and -cooled reactors appeared to be particularly attractive. In the course of the discussion that followed his paper, Professor Blokhintsev said that several shutdowns due to instruments not properly operating had occurred during the first one or two months of operation, but never since. He also confirmed a statement made by former Premier Georgi Malenkov the previous June, during a reception for Prime Minister Nehru at the Indian Embassy, that the Soviet Union was building a one-hundred-thousand-kilowatt nuclear power plant, which would be in operation in about a year.

Then it was Dr. Zinn's turn to deliver his paper. Walter Zinn was a reactor pioneer, for he had started working on uranium fission problems at Columbia University shortly after fission was discovered; when the Columbia group had moved to Chicago and built the first atomic pile there, he had gone along to supervise all phases of construction of the pile, and so he became the first atomic general contractor. Not long afterward, he was appointed director of the young Argonne National Laboratory and was still holding that post at the time of the conference. Walter Zinn, like the few other men who could claim to have spent a not insignificant portion of their lives with reactors, had confidence in them. It seemed to his listeners, that morning, that he was trying to transmit his confidence to them: tall and blond, he stood straight in front of the vast audience, read fast and precisely from his copy, with great assurance, smiling now and then with satisfaction. By contrast, the milder Professor Blokhintsev seemed retiring.

The nuclear power plant described by Zinn was constructed at the National Reactor Testing Station in Idaho, during the fall and winter of 1954–55, by scientists and engineers of the Argonne National Laboratory. It used a reactor of the boiling-water type, which simplified the process of transforming nuclear energy into electricity. In nuclear plants using other reactor designs the heat generated in the reactor was carried by the coolant to a heat exchanger where it produced steam. A reactor in which the water used as coolant was allowed to boil and form steam inside the reactor vessel eliminated the need for a heat exchanger. The steam generated by the reactor described by Zinn was either released to the atmosphere or delivered to a turbogenerator rated at thirty-five hundred kilowatts. The fuel was uranium enriched to about 90 per cent of U-235.

The plant was built to gain experience under various operating conditions, and the reactor was constructed in such a way that it was possible to change the entire core, including the control rods. The plant had been actually operated with different reactor cores. Although the last core had been in operation for only a short time, it had already produced three million kilowatt-hours of energy as steam. It had powered a turbogenerator producing twenty-three hundred kilowatts of electricity. The reactor had proved extremely safe under operating conditions, even when a much higher steam pressure than normal had been allowed to build up inside the vessel. The plant cost 550,000 dollars. A cost summary indicated that, depending on the price set for the uranium fuel, power would cost from thirty to thirty-five mills per kilowatt-hour, less than twice the cost of power produced by coal plants of the same size. The simplicity of construction, ease of operation, and low cost of this plant suggested that it would be suitable for use in remote areas or in conjunction with mining or manufacturing operations.

Dr. Zinn's detailed description of this plant and of its operation was only one instalment of a story that was disclosed at the Geneva conference. The instalment that chronologically ought to have preceded this one was told both in one of the technical films and in a paper delivered by Dr. Joseph R. Dietrich at another general session the day after Zinn had spoken. It related the series of experiments performed before the power plant was built, to determine how safe boiling-water reactors could be made. These experiments were called "Borax tests," Borax being short for Boiling Water Reactor Experiment. The persons who watched the film after having heard the paper realized that the narrator was Dr. Dietrich himself: the same quiet, unassuming voice related the same dramatic events with no trace of excitement, yet conveyed to the audience a sense of his competence and zeal. The events, as reconstructed from Dietrich's paper, film narration, and remarks, are about as follows.

Scientists had always been extremely conscious of reactor hazards, and in building reactors they had put much extra work into offsetting the presumed dangers. If one reactor design were to prove safe, they would be able to simplify its construction and avoid the extra work. They had assumed at first that boiling and steam formation would make reactors dangerously unstable. But then some scientists and engineers at the Argonne National Laboratory advanced the hypothesis that water-cooled and -moderated reactors where water *could* boil would be safe. If in one of them the nuclear chain reaction were to get out of control and the reactor power were to increase rapidly, the excess heat thus generated would make the water boil. Since the moderating water was necessary to keep the nuclear chain reaction going, any steam that diluted the water or shoved it out of the core would automatically slow or stop the reaction. In other words, the reactor would have self-regulating characteristics.

Early work toward proving this assumption was carried out on a small scale at the Argonne National Laboratory. The results were encouraging; however, the experiments could not be considered conclusive unless carried out on a larger scale, and this was not feasible in a laboratory. The National Reactor Testing Station in Idaho was on desert ground, at the foot of barren mountains, where more drastic experiments on reactors would not endanger the population. So a team of Argonne scientists and engineers, led by Zinn, moved to the testing station and joined forces with Harold Lichtenberger, Director of Argonne's Idaho Division.

Meanwhile, the idea had occurred to the scientists that, since boiling in a reactor would likely be safe, a reactor could be designed to boil and produce directly in its vessel the steam needed to operate a turbogenerator.

Experiments at the Idaho station started in the early summer of 1953. Cautiously, the first tests were made with a reactor, called Borax I, which had been constructed during the spring. The reactor consisted of a steel vessel shaped like a large milk bottle, half filled with water in which fuel elements and control rods were immersed. The vessel, four feet in diameter, was placed in a larger tank sunk part way into the ground, and earth was piled around it for shielding. The reactor was operated by remote control from a trailer located half a mile away. In addition to the regular control rods, it had a larger one that could be ejected very rapidly to simulate an accident. At first many experiments were performed letting out only a small portion of the large rod so that the water did not boil. The results were consistent from day to day; they proved that the men who had built the reactor fully understood what went on inside it and were in perfect control of it.

The experimenters went a little further; they ejected more of the rod, and the water boiled in the open vessel. The steam thus produced did not have enough pressure to generate electricity. So the next step was to put a lid on the vessel, with a small opening for a pressure-regulating valve, and to operate the reactor like a pressure cooker. At increasingly high pressures the reactor proved safe. If the large rod was suddenly expelled, the reactor produced steam in sufficient amounts to check the rise of power. In one experiment the power was increased tenfold in slightly more than one-hundredth of a second. The reactor became violent: it pushed water and steam out of the tank and up in the air, thirty feet high. The fuel plates in the core were deformed. But the violence was brief, the reactor shut itself down, with no intervention of automatic control mechanisms or of men.

Was the inherent safety of boiling-water reactors proved beyond doubt? Or was there a chance of an accident so violent that it would melt the fuel plates, disrupt the reactor structure, and let out radioactivity into the air? The chance was almost negligible under normal operating conditions, the scientists thought. Still, it was advisable to be prepared even for this remote possibility and to learn what was to be expected in such an accident. Borax I would be sacrificed: all the experiments that could be made with it had been performed, and the most useful thing it could still do was to let itself be destroyed. The sacrifice was consummated on July 22, 1954. Many visitors had come to the testing station to witness it, so great was the curiosity to see a reactor run away.

The control rod to be let out was a little larger than the previous ones; the springs to expel it were somewhat stronger. The rod was ejected by remote control from the trailer half a mile away. In two-tenths of a second it was almost entirely out of the reactor. The power developed in the core reached its peak. From the reactor a column of dark smoke eighty feet high rose against the bright sky over the desert. Then came the sound of an explosion. The smoke slowly cleared away, and the wreck of what had been the reactor came in sight: the superstructure and the control-rod mechanism had been carried away.

Cameras had taken still and motion pictures during the test. By examining the remains of the reactor and the pictures that had not been ruined by radiation, it was possible to reconstruct what had happened: The power had risen to more than ten million kilowatts. Most of the fuel plates had been melted. The molten metal in contact with water had caused a sharp rise in steam pressure, and this had burst open the reactor tank. Control mechanism and debris had been sent flying into the air. Yet, the explosion had not been too violent. It was comparable to that of a moderate amount of chemical explosive. It was evident that steam had terminated the nuclear power release at an early stage of the explosion and greatly attenuated the effects of the runaway. There was no appreciable radioactive fall-out at distances greater than a few hundred feet. This experiment could have been carried out on the grounds of the Argonne Laboratory, rather than among the cacti of the desert, without causing damage.

It was after the satisfactory destruction of Borax I that it was decided to build a larger Borax and to operate it to produce electricity in the way described in Walter Zinn's instalment of the Borax

story recounted earlier in this chapter. The third and last instalment
came out at Geneva a few days after the first two, in a press release
of the Atomic Energy Commission and in a film presented to the
United Nations: the electricity generated in the new plant at the
National Reactor Testing Station had been used to light and power
a town.

The plant had been operated with two reactor cores, Borax II and
Borax III, and had proved satisfactory. The next obvious thought
had been: "Well, why not supply a small city, just to complete the
experiment?" There was one the right size, only twenty miles away:
Arco, Idaho, population twelve thousand. From the testing station
an old, unused line connected with the Arco substation. Through
this line on July 17, 1955, Borax III supplied electricity to the city
of Arco. The utility lines feeding conventional electricity were dis-
connected, and for more than an hour Arco depended solely on
nuclear power.

The lighting of the city of Arco was a useful technical experiment.
The efficiency of a power plant cannot be proved until it feeds the
lines and supplies electricity for actual use. While a plant is designed to produce a certain amount of electricity, the amount consumed may vary. How would a decrease in power consumption in
Arco, for instance the turning-off of many lights at once, affect
Borax III at the testing station? It was expected that a drop in consumption would make the generator turn more easily and the turbine
speed up to a point where it might wreck itself. A governor was inserted. If the turbine were to move too fast, the governor would cut
the supply of steam. The steam, in this case, would not be let out of
the reactor but would build up pressure inside it. This pressure
might become dangerous. An operator was placed in charge of
watching the pressure inside the reactor and of taking the necessary
steps to avoid its excessive rise. Under operating conditions it was
found that pressure variations due to changes in electricity consumption were slow enough to give the operator sufficient time for the
necessary adjustments.

The film on the lighting of Arco was not included in the seven
technical films prepared by the OIC for regular showing during the
conference. Having been taken late, it was not translated into the
other languages, as the seven other films had been. It was shown

only once, for news representatives, while the other seven, and the popular film "A Is for Atom," prepared by the United States Information Agency, were shown daily, in one language or another, in alternation with films prepared by other countries.

Borax III was not the first reactor to produce electricity in the United States: an experimental breeder reactor built at the same testing station in Idaho by Argonne people had produced one hundred kilowatts of electricity as a demonstration in December, 1951, and was the first reactor to have produced electricity in the world. Since its initial operation, the reactor was used routinely as the power source for the Argonne site at the National Reactor Testing Station.

In February, 1953, electricity was again produced as a demonstration at the Oak Ridge National Laboratory with a reactor of a different type, a homogeneous experimental reactor.

About the time when the city of Arco was being lighted by electricity produced with Borax III, a submarine prototype reactor was converted to production of power for civilian uses; at West Milton, New York, the land-based prototype for the second atomic submarine, the "Sea Wolf," generated electricity that was sent into homes and industries. The occasion was marked by a ceremony which started, like most ceremonies, with a speech—it was delivered by Admiral Strauss. The ceremony went on, however, in a less formal manner, as Mr. Strauss and others in his party cooked hamburgers with atomic power.

It became clear at Geneva that several countries had already embarked on well-defined programs of atomic power production; that at least four of them—France, Great Britain, the Soviet Union, and the United States—were already building full-scale power plants; and that in making their plans each country had gone its own way, according to need and preference. Most striking in this respect was the contrast between the United States and England, which, having started together and joined their efforts during the war, had then traveled along diverging roads in peacetime. Sir John Cockcroft stressed the reasons for these differences in his evening lecture, in which he summarized what was learned at the conference. He said:

"Great Britain is an example of a highly industrialized country with small hydroelectric resources, with poor prospects of any substantial increase in coal production and with rapidly increasing demand for electricity and other forms of energy. So *early* nuclear power development is essential for Britain—it comes only just in time for us—and we believe that by 1975 almost half our electricity will be developed from nuclear power.

"The United States presents a *different* picture of a great industrial country with very great reserves of easily worked coal and also oil and natural gas. Their speakers have said that the use of nuclear energy in *their* country will depend mainly on its cost relative to power from coal. So they think that by 1975 the production of power generated from nuclear energy will be between 1 per cent and 15 per cent of their total power depending on whether costs are 9 mills a unit or 6 mills a unit. . . ."

With more money for research and less incentive for immediate realization of atomic power, the United States could afford to consider the long-range goal above the short-range. Before entering the production stage, it undertook a wide and thorough experimental program to solve technological problems and determine relative merits of different reactor approaches from the point of view of safety and economy. Various types of reactors had been studied, and each had been developed by small steps, building an "experiment" first, then a small reactor producing little or no power, then larger ones. Out of the many designs, the government had selected the five types believed to be the most likely to lead to economic nuclear power and was developing them under a five-year program. Only one of them, the Pressurized Water Reactor at Shippingport, Pennsylvania, was to be a full-scale plant, and its construction was undertaken in an experimental spirit, to gain knowledge from its functioning.

While many people in the United States felt that the greatest benefits to their country from atomic energy would come from isotopes for quite a few years ahead, the British had no doubts that for them the most valuable peaceful application of the atom was prompt production of power. So they worked at it as fast as they could. They had a late start. They had undertaken an independent atomic energy program at home only after the end of the war, and their first reactor, Gleep (for Graphite Low-Energy Experimental

Pile), was completed almost five years after the Chicago pile, to which it was very similar. They built a second experimental pile, Bepo (British Experimental Pile), on the same principles and cooled it with air. Although Bepo was never intended to be a prototype power reactor, some of the heat that it generated was used to warm laboratory buildings at Harwell. The British liked this type of reactor and preferred to perfect its design and develop it industrially rather than try several different approaches.

Early in 1953 the British Minister of Supply announced that his government was considering the construction of an experimental atomic station, and, the following summer, work began at Calder Hall near Windscale in Cumberland on two power reactors that were to feed one hundred thousand kilowatts into the national grid by 1956. Another pair was later authorized. (In the United States, work on the Shippingport plant, the first full-scale power plant, started in September, 1954.)

A paper on the Calder Hall plant was read by Sir Christopher Hinton, Managing Director of the United Kingdom Atomic Energy Authority. A balding, white-haired man with fine features, he let the corners of his mouth drop down in ironical expression, especially if questions were asked that might be interpreted as casting doubts on the wisdom of some British nuclear undertakings. The reactors at Calder Hall were gas cooled, graphite moderated, and burned natural uranium. The advantages of this reactor type, said Sir Christopher, lay in the fact that it was extremely safe, even in as densely populated a country as England, and that it did not require enriched fuel or "expensive and exotic materials of construction." "It can perhaps be regarded as the slow speed reciprocating engine of the reactor world, reliable and almost conventional in design."

Reactors using natural uranium as fuel produced plutonium as a by-product. Plutonium could be used in atomic weapons and was therefore of great military value. But in an entirely civilian program this fact should not be taken into account, and, to make plutonium valuable, other uses should be found for it. To prove that plutonium could be advantageously employed for power production, the British decided to build a fast breeder reactor burning plutonium, at Dounray on the northern coast of Scotland. If the Calder Hall type of power reactor was conservative, the Dounray was one of the most advanced and could be regarded, in Sir Christopher Hinton's words, as "the gas turbine of the nuclear reactor world." So England had covered the distance between the most conservative and the most advanced reactor in one jump.

Like England, France had embarked on an atomic power program calling for the development of gas-cooled, graphite-moderated reactors burning natural uranium. Work on an industrial center had started in late 1953 at Marcoule near Avignon, in the valley of the Rhône River. A first pile, producing five thousand kilowatts of electricity was almost completed, and two larger ones had been designed for construction at the same center. They were to produce both electricity and plutonium.

France had undertaken its atomic program against greater odds than England. Before the Second World War, French scientists had made important contributions to the advancement of nuclear science, but the war and the German occupation had disrupted research, impoverished the country, and prevented France from sharing in the spectacular achievements of its allies in the atomic field. At the end of the war the United States, Great Britain, and Canada controlled almost entirely the uranium mined in the free world. The French Atomic Energy Commission was then established to start an atomic program and an atomic industry from scratch, without the benefit of Anglo-American know-how. It succeeded in all phases, from the prospecting of uranium and the opening of uranium mines both in the home country and in the overseas territories to the design and construction of plants for the purification of uranium and the separation of plutonium. Zoe, the first French research pile, was put into operation at the end of 1948. By the time of the Geneva conference, France was self-sufficient in atomic materials and expected to become a producer in the world market of uranium and thorium. The French High Commissioner for Atomic Energy, Professor Francis Perrin, was in Geneva both as one of France's five official representatives and as a vice-president of the conference. In the halls of the Palais he was well known, for his thin, U-shaped beard hemming his jaw from ear to ear, and the large, intelligent nose overshadowing a small mustache made him easily recognizable in the diversified crowd of delegates. In talking about the atomic program of his country, Francis Perrin let out a flow of rapid words, in the typical French manner, and his eyes lit up suddenly, betraying his satisfaction.

The Soviets did not describe a development "program" and did not say what they had in mind to build after the full-scale plant under construction, to be completed in 1956, of the same design as the smaller one described in Professor Blokhintsev's paper.

Other countries had constructed and operated reactors: Canada had two reactors for research in operation, and an experimental one for study on power development was at an advanced stage of construction. Sweden had a research reactor. Norway and Holland had jointly built a research reactor at Kjeller, Norway, and thus had set the pattern and the first example for possible co-operation among nations in the development of an atomic program. And in more countries reactors were under construction.

The state of atomic industry in the world, as seen at the Geneva conference, can be summarized as follows: of the power plants either in operation or under construction, some utilized highly pure natural uranium as fuel and some utilized enriched uranium. Only four countries could refine uranium to the required degree of purity and fabricate it into elements: the United States, the Soviet Union, Great Britain, and France. The first two of these nations were developing reactors using enriched uranium, while Great Britain and France had undertaken to build an industry based at first on natural uranium. Enriched uranium is obtained in separation plants which are very expensive and cumbersome. France had not built one, and could not enrich fuel. Britain, which could produce enriched fuel in a gaseous diffusion separation plant, had started its atomic power program before this plant was working at full rate. The United States, Great Britain, and the Soviet Union were able to separate plutonium from spent elements and reprocess the used fuel. France had devised a method for separating plutonium and was ready to build a plant for this purpose at the industrial center of Marcoule.

Like the United States and the Soviet Union, several other countries illustrated their atomic programs through exhibits. At the Palais des Nations the most extensive exhibits of these other countries were those of the United Kingdom and of France. The British technical exhibit was strictly and severely scientific and included only reactor models and instruments. The instruments had been developed by the British Atomic Energy Authority's Research and Industrial Groups for reactor control, for special recording work, and for dealing with the raw materials of the atomic age.

If the technical exhibit seemed somewhat overwhelming and restricted in scope, that at the Palais des Expositions was not. Set up on the spacious mezzanine, it was the largest, and possibly the best organized, there. It was divided in two parts: the first was the Atomic Energy Authority's survey of its achievements in building up an atomic organization and of its efforts in exploiting peaceful uses to the fullest. The second was a wide commercial display organized by British firms associated with atomic development.

Where the first part began, large, eye-catching models and panels illustrated the structure of the atomic nucleus and the process of fission. (In all countries the difficulty of explaining atomic science in a popular way had taxed the artists' imagination to the limit. At the exhibit of the United States Information Agency, a diagram of a cow on a wall panel showed the path that food took inside her body after she ate radioactive plants: lights of different colors went on along her digestive tract, her circulatory system, and in her milk. In a panel at the excellent Swiss exhibit, merrily scintillating electrons collected inside a beaker.) From fission, the British exhibit led the layman to the development and utilization of atomic energy, to beautifully landscaped reactor models and to presentation of uses of radioisotopes in the industries, in medicine, and in agricultural research.

In the commercial section an industrial group, consisting of three prominent firms, advertised that through its co-operative effort atomic power plants of the Calder Hall type could be built anywhere in the world under a single contract—but back at the Palais des Nations both Cockcroft and Hinton stated that England was not yet prepared to sell reactors or even to quote prices. At a press conference Hinton warned that reactors were complicated machines, safer, in the early stages, in countries with a well-developed technology. Other nations ought to wait, have a few years of training, and then, perhaps in the early 1960's, purchase reactors of the Calder Hall type, which by that time would be ready for sale.

Both the technical and the commercial French exhibits were organized by a young French woman, Mlle Huguette Batsh, who, despite a degree in mathematics, had retained a feminine and French taste for the aesthetics of things. Her exhibits were modernistic in design and effectively laid out. The commercial display was put up mostly by the various exhibiting French industries, she said, giving the impression that she had the technical more at heart. Mlle Batsh had not been spared the anxieties due to shortness of time. The French technical exhibit caused much concern not only to her but to the United Nations as well, because of its persistent absence during the days preceding the conference. It arrived at the Palais at last, forty-eight hours before the opening of all exhibits. It was ready on time.

Huguette Batsh's satisfaction was evident, despite her shyness and the quietness of her manners. In acompanying visitors, while walking over the large gray and white linoleum squares of the floor, she would point out various achievements of French technical proficiency: a proton-synchroton which, she said, would be the most powerful of its kind; a tube made of beryllium, the best ever fabricated; a model of Saclay, the French center for nuclear research; and pictures of the industrial station at Marcoule. Meanwhile, if asked, she would talk a little, almost reluctantly, about herself and her career. She had been the *professeur* in charge of training personnel for petroleum industries. Companies like Esso and Shell were small in France and did not have their own schools. Mlle Batsh set up the training program and taught for six years. But once the program was well established, it seemed to be going on by itself and became routine. She lost interest in it and quit in 1954. She joined the staff of the information office of the French Atomic Energy Commission, and in that capacity she was asked to organize the exhibits. Perhaps the piece in which she showed the greatest pride was a geological map of France with little glowing lights that indicated uranium deposits being mined. No other country, she stressed, indicated the location of its deposits with the same degree of candor.

This remark leads up to a few considerations that may fittingly conclude this chapter. Although only the French geological map was displayed at Geneva, a great wealth of information on the natural occurrence of uranium and thorium was submitted to the conference:

ninety-four papers (two-thirds of them from the United States) and numerous publications from twenty-three countries. They were not presented orally for lack of time, but all were reviewed in a single paper by Professor P. H. Kerr of the United Nations. From this paper; from a paper read by Dr. Jesse C. Johnson, Director of the Division of Raw Materials of the United States Atomic Energy Commission; and from a panel discussion in which twelve countries participated, a general picture of widespread occurrence and of plentifulness of uranium emerged. Nuclear fuel was abundant, and sufficient to meet demands for a long time.

A large part of the geological data disclosed at the conference had been secret up to then. Once published in the proceedings of the conference, they would constitute an invaluable source of information for many years to come: Jesse Johnson remarked that, while reactor technology was likely to undergo drastic changes in the future, the geology of the world would always remain what it was.

11 RADIATION HAZARDS

Scientists in Geneva were usually in agreement about the main scientific questions, a fact which made the task of the reporters easy; after interviewing several people, newspapermen added up the information and wrote their articles. They got so used to unanimity that when they found divergence of opinions in one field they were quite unhappy. They talked to the physicists and the engineers, and these belittled the dangers to populations due to operation of large power plants and the consequent handling of great quantities of radioactivity. They talked to the biologists, and these expressed concern. As a reporter aptly put it, the makers of radioactivity were much more optimistic than the geneticists. And if the scientists were in disagreement, how could the press give the public a sound picture of radiation risks?

The remark about the optimism of the radiation-makers came up during the already mentioned press conference held by Sir Christopher Hinton. He was asked what he thought about the hazards deriving from the disposal of radioactive wastes, and he answered that he was not in the least worried. The problem mainly concerned not power plants but chemical separation plants, and these were few and "in isolated situations." In England it was expected that chemical reprocessing would be done in one or two or, "at the outside," three factories under the Atomic Energy Authority's control. The bulk of the fission products of great activity, currently stored, were finding more and more uses, Sir Christopher said, and so there would be fewer wastes. The problem might be of diminishing importance.

Hinton then mentioned the fact that in England some wastes of weak activity were discharged into the sea, and the question was asked whether England had consulted with other countries about this radioactivity that went into the ocean. The answer was that the activity stayed well below the international standards of tolerance; that no fission products were discharged into the ocean; that the contribution in radioactivity from a well-managed industrial plant was quite negligible; that a well-managed industrial power program of considerable size could be so operated as to constitute no danger, no condition that needed even to be studied by geneticists.

Sir George Thomson, who was present at the press conference and had taken part in the previous discussion, came to Hinton's aid and said that the level of natural radioactivity due to all causes—rocks containing radioactive minerals, cosmic rays, etc.—varies from region to region of the world; that the water in New York is five times more radioactive than Sir Christopher Hinton was allowed to make the sea water; that the activity due to cosmic radiation is greater at high altitudes than at sea level, yet the Swiss living more than one thousand meters above sea level do not consider themselves in genetic danger; that an increase of 10 per cent in the radiation level in London would not bring it equal to that of the Swiss mountains.

Sir Christopher Hinton's confidence left the reporters somewhat doubtful. The reader will do well to pause and take stock of the situation.

Reactor men and physicists did not deny the potential hazards of radiation; they concurred in the opinion that further studies of radiation effects on men were in order. They pointed out, however, that people took for granted and accepted as unavoidable other risks brought about by modern civilization. Nobody, they said, had ever thought of limiting the production of automobiles on the grounds that exhaust fumes might be harmful in the long run, that their possible consequences to future generations were not known. The potential dangers in the atomic industry were comparable to those of other new fields of technology; and the fact that the atomic industry was closely watched by scientists gave it a privileged position over other industries.

The biological effects of radiations can be broadly divided into two classes: the direct effects on exposed individuals, and the indirect effects on their descendants through genetic mutations.

The direct effects of excessive exposure to radiations are much more evident than the genetic and were recognized first. The circumstances were recalled at Geneva. Professor Roentgen discovered X-rays in the latter part of 1895. By the end of the following January, one of the men working with X-ray tubes had developed a peculiar irritation of the skin on his hands. At once it was determined that the irritation was due to exposure to X-rays. Soon it was found that X-rays could cause other injuries to workers and to experimental animals: they made eyes smart, caused hair to fall, produced nausea and vomiting. Handling of radioactive substances like radium could also produce some of these symptoms.

In 1900, in an experimental spirit, Pierre Curie exposed his arm to radium and studied the resulting burn. Both he and his wife, Marie Curie, after having handled active materials for some time, reported inflammation, hardening, and scaling of the skin on the tips of their fingers. Henri Becquerel, the discoverer of radioactivity, carried some radium in a small glass tube inside his vest pocket and was burned by it.

Within the next twelve or fifteen years the list of radiation injuries grew: damage could be produced with X-rays in most organs of the body (it is now known that large doses of X-rays can affect all organs); cancer could develop in old X-ray scars; changes could appear in the blood and in the bone marrow; sterility could be produced in experimental animals; and two workers with X-rays developed anemia.

While the need for protection against the effects of radiations was obvious, no general measures were taken until the First World War, when the diagnostic use of X-rays became widespread. A British X-ray and Radium Protection Committee was then established, and not long afterward the International Commission on Radiological Protection came into being. Their studies were aimed at determining the doses to which various parts of the body could be exposed without suffering injury, and the dose to which the entire body could be exposed indefinitely, in occupations involving work with radiations. The first recommendations of the International Commission were based on studies of groups of individuals who had been occupationally exposed to radiations for some years and showed no ill effects. They were directed mostly at the medical profession and, to a lesser degree, at the luminous-dial painters.

The scope of these studies suddenly broadened in 1942, when the first chain-reacting pile started to operate. Immediately recognized were the potential dangers of neutrons from the fission process and of other radiations, especially gamma rays, from fission products. In the greatly intensified research on the biological effects of radiations more facts came to light.

It was found that radiation effects on the blood were not limited to the marked changes in blood counts due to real overexposures as observed in radiologists and radium workers in the early days, but that some changes in the number or in the shape of the blood corpuscles could be produced by small radiation doses of short duration. At the time of the conference it had not been ascertained whether these smaller changes have any significance for the health of the individuals. Meanwhile, a study of the causes of death of radiologists who had died during the twenty years between 1928 and 1948 had revealed that the incidence of leukemia among them had been nine times greater than among other physicians who had not worked with X-rays.

It was known even before 1942 that treatment with large doses of X-rays could produce cataracts in the eyes; and when in 1920 Mme Curie was told by her doctor that a double cataract was threatening her sight, the thought occurred to her at once that perhaps radium had something to do with it. In the years following the Second World War it was realized that changes in the lens of the eye could be caused by neutrons and that smaller doses of neutrons than of X-rays were sufficient to produce these changes.

Another effect of radiations was reported at Geneva by Dr. Robert J. Hasterlik of the Argonne Cancer Research Hospital. He read a paper on the clinical observations on four patients who had been exposed to large quantities of radiations because of an accident. All four had shown a large and persistent increase in the quantities and numbers of amino acids excreted in their urine. Aminoaciduria appeared very soon after exposure and persisted long after other symptoms had stopped (some changes in the blood leukocytes, however, lasted longer than the aminoaciduria). Dr. Hasterlik believed that aminoaciduria might prove to be a sensitive and early indicator of overexposure. Its significance to the patients' health was not determined.

The effect of radiations on the lifespan of animals was ascertained: prolonged exposure to low-level radiation could shorten the average life of experimental animals. Statistical studies of this kind are not possible on men because the human lifespan varies so much

from one individual to another that any small variations from causes
other than natural cannot be detected.

On the basis of the accumulated knowledge, the International
Commission on Radiological Protection recommended 0.3 roentgens
per week as the maximum weekly dose for workers occupationally
exposed to radiation (for comparison, an accidental dose of 300 to
500 roentgens could be fatal). It may be of interest to note that the
Soviet Union, although not a member of the Commission on Radiological Protection, had accepted its recommendations and had arrived at the same value for the maximum weekly dose through independent work, according to a paper read by Professor F. G. Krotov.
The International Commission also made other recommendations,
for exposures of parts of the body only, for concentration of radioactivity in the air and water, and for other radiation doses and uses.

These recommendations were followed in the major atomic establishments, and it was the general consensus among biologists and
health physicists at Geneva that workers were quite adequately protected from the direct effects of radiations. Anyone who had the opportunity to glance at the magic world of one of these establishments
could not but be impressed by the protective measures that he saw
enforced: the badges worn by all to record exposure; the large signs
reading "Danger Radiation" wherever there were radioactive substances, even on hampers for contaminated clothes; the rubbers worn
in areas where there might be radioactivity on the floors; the counters to measure hand and foot radioactivity; the radioisotopes being
separated and bottled, and the bottles being inclosed in protective
lead containers, and these being placed on a conveyor belt behind
thick shielding walls, all by remote control; the plastic clothing, like
divers' suits, to be worn in contaminated areas; the long instruments
to handle materials under water, among them cans of food exposed
to the radiation of spent fuel elements in food-irradiation experiments; and the engaging smile with which directors of laboratories
would say: "The important thing is to keep everything perfectly
clean; you could eat off these floors!"

Some concern was expressed for other groups of people exposed
to radiations. It was pointed out, for instance, that some medical
practices of X-ray treatment and diagnosis might have to be revised
in the light of recent findings. Dr. Dwight E. Clark of the Argonne

Cancer Research Hospital reported a relatively high incidence of cancer of the thyroid in children and adolescents who were subjected in infancy and early childhood to X-ray treatment for benign conditions in the neck region such as whooping cough, enlarged tonsils, and enlarged thymus.

Dr. Liane B. Russell related experiments that she and her husband performed on thousands of pregnant mice at Oak Ridge and that showed the very harmful effects of X-rays on embryos. Interpreting the meaning of these experiments for human beings, the Russells stated that embryos are very sensitive to radiation in the early stages of the mother's pregnancy, when pregnancy may still be unsuspected. They recommended that "whenever possible, pelvic irradiation of women of child bearing age should be restricted to the two weeks following the menses," when there is comparatively little chance of unsuspected pregnancy.

The group reported as exposed to perhaps the greatest radiation risks were workers in certain uranium mines. Uranium ores contain radium, which emits spontaneously a gaseous substance called radon. The concentration of radon in uranium mines, especially in poorly ventilated galleries, exceeded that recommended by the International Commission on Radiation Protection. Following blasting operations, the concentration of radon in the air became many times higher; under certain circumstances radon became dissolved in water, and through fissures it seeped out of galleries into the surroundings. It was, however, stated that these conditions would be soon improved with adequate ventilation and with other protective measures.

It was the prevailing opinion at Geneva that the direct biological effects of radiations on individuals were well under control. There was more concern and less agreement about the indirect effects that continued exposure of large sections of populations to low levels of radiation might have upon the genetic composition of future generations. Because it was to some extent controversial, the "genetic question" aroused enormous interest; not only scientists, but also, and perhaps even more, laymen discussed it; reporters went back to it in interviews and press conferences; newspapers gave space and attention to it; and it was followed up at the United Nations level after the conference.

We shall try to give an idea of the range of opinions expressed at Geneva, without attempting to evaluate them.

The evolution of mankind has taken place in the presence of spontaneous radioactivity. It was stressed at Geneva that man's environment has always been radioactive because of cosmic rays, radioactive substances contained in the rocks, naturally occurring radioisotopes of potassium and carbon, the radon always present in the air, and small but detectable amounts of radium deposited in the bones. This "background" radioactivity is not uniform: the intensity of cosmic rays is greater at high altitudes than at low, and the radioactive content of rocks varies from one region of the earth to another.

Very interesting investigations of natural background radiation were carried out in Sweden and reported in a paper read by Professor Rolf M. Sievert. Swedish scientists had driven from place to place in an ambulance, which was exhibited in the gardens of the Palais des Nations near the United States Radiological Unit and which was mentioned in the chapter on the technical exhibits. They had measured the concentration of radium in the pipe water of a Swedish city, the differences of background radioactivity inside Swedish homes constructed of varying materials, and the amount of radiation that different people gave off spontaneously owing to the radioactive substances inside their bodies. This radiation was found to be a little higher than average, but not much, in people living in a city where the radium content in the water was five times greater than that in Stockholm.

Later the Swedish radiologists built a low-background laboratory just outside Stockholm and measured the natural radioactivity emitted by children of a nearby school, by middle-aged persons from a commercial enterprise, and by old people from a home for the aged. They found that men emitted more gamma rays than women, which, they said, was to be expected, because women have more fat and less muscle, and radioactive potassium is deposited in muscle tissue. Old people emitted fewer gamma rays than young people because their muscles were atrophied.

In 1927 Professor Herman J. Muller discovered that radiations can cause genetic mutations. From then on geneticists have asserted that a part of the spontaneous mutations occurring in all living organisms are due to the background radiation. It was calculated that the background radioactivity was giving each human being a radiation dose of three to six roentgens during his reproductive life and that this dose was probably responsible for between 8 and 16 per cent of the spontaneous mutations. Geneticists believe that a rise in the level of the background radioactivity would raise the number of mutations in the germ cells of the human population.

The fundamentals of radiation genetics were expounded in a paper prepared for the conference by Dr. Muller. As gathered from this paper and from those read orally at Geneva, the basic ideas are as follows:

A mutation is a change that occurs in the chemical composition of a gene, one of the very numerous hereditary units existing in each cell. Such a change may happen from natural causes; it is a rare event, but one from which there is no going back: once the change has taken place it stays there. At cell division each gene duplicates itself and each daughter cell receives genes exactly alike. So, if a cell contained a mutant gene before division, the mutation persists in the daughter cells and in the cells formed in successive divisions. By this mechanism, a mutation that takes place in a gene of a reproductive cell is inherited by individuals of successive generations.

The human body is such an extremely complicated and well-adjusted machine that any change in its genetic constitution is much more likely to be harmful than beneficial. Geneticists believe that over 99 per cent of all mutations are detrimental and will bring an impairment of function. Yet evolution of mankind has presumably taken place as a result of spontaneous mutations selected naturally in the presence of pressures of the environment. On the very rare occasions when a mutant gene has produced an advantageous change, "the resultant individual, just because it was aided by that mutation, tended to multiply more than the others." Individuals of subsequent generations who had that mutation also multiplied more than others and their type spread. Types more adapted to the environment supplanted the type that had been the normal one before. At the same time natural selection acted on the much more numerous mutations that were disadvantageous, through a process of slow elimination.

Disadvantageous mutations impair fitness of the individual and in the long run cause either premature death or sterility in some descendant. In both cases this ultimate descendant does not reproduce, and the mutation is no longer passed on. This is called a "genetic death." Through genetic death of all the individuals who have inherited a mutation, this mutation is eventually eliminated.

There is a factor greatly slowing the process of elimination: each individual receives his genes from both parents, so that usually a mutant gene becomes paired with the normal corresponding gene from the other parent. A mutant gene is usually recessive and the normal corresponding gene, being dominant, has a stronger effect. Hence a mutation may persist for many generations, although it is its fate to cause suffering and ultimately genetic death.

Any population contains an accumulation or "load" of natural mutations. If the rate at which mutations arise and that at which they are eliminated remain constant for several generations, the population reaches a genetic equilibrium: as many mutations are eliminated through genetic death as are created anew, and the load of mutations does not increase. If, for some reason, the number of mutations per generation increases, or if the elimination through genetic death decreases, mutations accumulate in the population, and the load of mutations becomes greater.

Geneticists fear that both the factors working toward genetic equilibrium might be adversely affected by modern civilization: the development of a world-wide atomic industry may raise the level of background radioactivity, which in its turn may raise the number of new mutations per generation. On the other hand, medicine and the modern aids to civilized living may slow down the natural elimination of detrimental mutations. Physicians are already saving many lives that would otherwise be lost through genetic death; moreover, the pressures of the environment are being immensely relieved, for man has to a large degree adapted the environment to his needs, rather than his needs to the environment as all other animals have. It is anybody's guess what the chances of survival for the human race would be if we were suddenly to revert to dwelling in caves and to other primitive customs.

It was recognized at the conference that, with the peaceful developments of the atomic age, small sections of populations would be exposed to relatively high radiation doses in the course of work, radiological examinations and treatments, and because of accidents. For the genetic future of mankind, these small sections are less important than the large sections that may become exposed to an increased low-level background radiation. Geneticists expressed concern for any increase of this background level, no matter how small, for they believed that there is no "threshold" or radiation level below which radiations produce no genetic effect. The effects of radiation are cumulative, and what counts is the average total amount of radiation that reaches the individuals' gonads during their reproductive life.

Geneticists tried to determine what exposure rate would double the natural mutation rate. Opinions diverged somewhat, and the figure that was perhaps quoted more often was fifty roentgens per generation. This means that a population that had received this dose for many generations "would at last have twice as many ills of genetic origin as we have. Yet we already have more than enough for our comfort," as Dr. Muller stated in his paper. "All these questions need to be . . . investigated far more realistically than they have in the past. Otherwise we may at last find ourselves, genetically, facing a parallel to already accomplished deforestation and erosion, on even a grander scale."

This warning was echoed, one way or another, in several papers on the genetic effects of radiation. Dr. T. C. Carter of the United Kingdom Atomic Energy Research Establishment, spoke on "The Genetic Problem of Irradiated Human Populations" and highlighted some of the great uncertainties encountered by geneticists in any attempt to evaluate the genetic dangers quantitatively. By way of introduction to his paper he made an ethical consideration: in modern civilization, he said, people are willing to take risks, like those of airplane traveling, provided they can evaluate the risk and have free choice to expose or refuse to expose themselves to it. In the case of genetic hazards from radiations there is no possibility either of evaluation or of free choice; even the informed disagree about the nature and the magnitude of genetic risk, and the unlucky individual suffering genetic damage is not the one who exposed himself.

Dr. Carter then went on to explain how geneticists trying to assess genetic damage quantitatively were faced with enormous gaps in the knowledge of the genetics of human populations. And, not being able to experiment on men, they resorted to the fruit fly and the mouse. (Even if man were willing to be the guinea pig, his life is so long that he is not fitted for genetic investigations, which require statistical studies on many successive generations.) From the results of studies on animals, geneticists constructed mathematical models intended to represent human populations and using these models tried to evaluate the damage of radiations to men. In so doing they were forced to estimate several quantities that were not mathematically measurable: the number of genes in each cell, the rate of spontaneous mutations, the proportion of all deaths that were "genetic deaths." When they gave numerical values to these quantities and calculated the number of genetic deaths due to a given dose of radiation per generation, they obtained figures which varied by a factor of at least one thousand.

"Granted that any increase in radiation exposure will ultimately cause some genetic deaths," Dr. Carter said, "the form which they will take should be considered. In very few cases is it possible to specify the form and make numerical estimates." The great majority of mutations are not easily recognized. Not all are necessarily harmful to the population even though they may cause genetic death of the individual. "The existence of a negative correlation between fertility and intelligence, and the fact that intelligence is at least partly genetically determined, implies that an unduly high proportion of the most intelligent suffer genetic death. . . . If genetic death is the price of being a Beethoven or an Isaac Newton, it does not necessarily follow that all genetic deaths are undesirable." (The scientific soundness of this statement was questioned by American biologists.)

Carter believed that a research program aiming at accurate quantitative predictions of the effects of chronic exposure to radiation should fall into three parts: "research on mutation, since radiation induces mutations; research on animal populations, since man is a social animal; and research on human populations, since one cannot justify the application to one species of quantitative measurements made on another." Commenting about the third part of the research, Dr. Carter said that the first thing we need to know is the extent of genetic death in a civilized population and the form it takes. Does it occur through difficulty in staying alive before or after birth, through susceptibility to infections, through disinclination to marry or to reproduce? Is it associated with intelligence or mental defects? To what extent does it cause suffering? Next we need to know the relationship in man between radiation exposure and mutation rate. The best way, in his opinion, would be to study populations living in zones where the natural radiation background is high, like some granite areas of Scotland, England, and Scandinavia. "Such a project," Dr. Carter concluded, "would probably have to be on an international scale and would certainly take ten years or more; but I think the results would be well worth the effort."

Dr. Carter's agnostic attitude toward the genetic problem of radiation seemed to place him midway between the pessimists, represented by most of the geneticists, and the optimists. Typical among the latter were "the makers of radioactivity" like Sir Christopher Hinton. But trustful voices were heard from other quarters also: Sir Ernest Rock-Carling of the United Kingdom Home Office spiced his not entirely optimistic paper with such remarks as, ". . . The powers of recovery and repair developed in the course of evolution are inherent in the live cell itself however menaced. . . . It would look as if the 0.5 or even 0.1 of beneficial mutations grudgingly allowed by geneticists had been extremely potent. . . . 'Bad' genes . . . can be good in certain circumstances and combinations. . . . The gene that transmits liability to sickle cell anemia seems to confer immunity to a form of malaria. . . ."

Dr. Binks of the United Kingdom Radiological Protection Service and secretary of the International Commission on Radiological Protection said: ". . . It may be of interest to note that in the United Kingdom estimates have been made of the total dose received by all radiological workers and of the total dose received by the gonads of all males and females during diagnostic examinations which take place before the age of about 30 years. Averaging these totals over the entire population, it is found that the dose per capita per generation of 30 years is less . . . than one thirtieth of the natural radiation level from cosmic and terrestrial sources. The additional genetic load is thus insignificant at the moment."

Optimistic views were expressed also outside the lecture halls. Senator Anderson held a press conference in his small hotel bedroom, where over fifty reporters were packed like sardines. When he was asked what he thought about radiation hazards, he answered that in the United States the hazard was found not to be so great as people thought. That the background radiation in Albuquerque, New Mexico, was five times as great as in Phoenix, Arizona, and that people in Albuquerque were quite healthy all the same.

Even more reassuring than these remarks were the quiet hopes, hinted at rather than fully spelled out at the conference, that in a few years ways might be found to prevent and cure some of the damage done by radiation to tissues and cells. Two papers were read on this subject, one by the Belgian Dr. Maisin, and the other by Dr. Alexander Hollaender of the Oak Ridge National Laboratory, who also gave an evening lecture. The lecture, reviewing the work done in numerous laboratories of the world and the state of knowledge, was illuminating, not only because it brought out facts, little known to the public, on the mechanism of radiation injury and of repair, but also because it showed how biological research was carried out, small step by small step, from the very simple to the extremely complicated. The first observations directed at understanding what really happens when radiation enters cells and tissues were made on a very simple biological compound, water. Studies of radiation effects on chromosomes were carried out on certain plants, like Tradescantia, in which the small number and large size of chromosomes facilitated observations. Attempts at increasing the resistance to radiation were first made on micro-organisms, bacteria and spores, only later on mammals—small mammals like mice. Researches on possible ways to prevent the mutations due to irradiation had so far been limited to bacteria.

The effects of X-rays on water could be modified by lowering the temperature and by eliminating the oxygen in it. These same factors raised the resistance to radiation of micro-organisms. The decrease of oxygen concentration protected mammals also: it was found that mice irradiated in an atmosphere of low oxygen content developed some resistance to X-ray exposure. Such an atmosphere would cause symptoms of oxygen deficiency in men and cause them serious troubles. A more promising way to protect man from radiation was through the use of reducing agents, namely, substances capable of combining with oxygen. Many reducing agents that worked successfully on micro-organisms were toxic to men, but cysteine, cysteamine, and thiuronium seemed promising for practi-

cal use and were under study in various countries. Thiuronium, prepared at Dr. Hollaender's laboratory in Oak Ridge, appeared the
most easily controlled. Dr. Hollaender expressed the hope that in a
year or two it would be possible to decide whether thiuronium could
be safely used on human beings.

All these compounds were effective only if administered before or
during irradiation, not after. In other words, their administration
was a protective measure and did not affect recovery. There were,
however, some ways of influencing recovery also. Some spontaneous
recovery from radiation effects could take place in animals, as was
indicated by the fact that animals could tolerate a larger total
amount of radiation if this was received in successive partial doses,
with intervals in between, rather than all at once. And recovery
could be helped. Experiments on irradiated mice had shown that, if
after exposure the spleen of non-irradiated mice was implanted, the
number of survivors greatly increased. These experiments had been
prompted by the observation that a surprisingly large number of
animals survived irradiation if their spleen had been shielded. Bone
marrow had also been used successfully in treatment of mice shortly
after irradiation, and several nutritive substances were found to be
of help.

Very good results had been obtained with the combined use of
preventive chemicals, before and during irradiation of mice and
transplantation of spleen afterward. The lethal dose for certain
strains of radiation-resistant mice had been tripled; while normally
about eight hundred roentgens would kill half the exposed mice,
about twenty-four hundred roentgens were needed to kill half the
mice that were submitted to the treatment.

The elimination of oxygen and the use of reducing substances
protected cells from genetic damage also. Dr. Hollaender had found
that when he managed to make bacteria stay alive after irradiation,
both by protection before exposure and treatment afterward, he also
reduced the number of mutations: the larger the number of cells
that he kept alive, the smaller the number of mutations. So it was
proved possible to do something to limit the number of radiation-
induced mutations, at least in some bacteria. If this finding were
applicable to men, it could be of considerable importance for the
future of mankind, Dr. Hollaender said. Unfortunately, he was in no

position to say whether his method would work on men. Experiments on mammals had been undertaken in his laboratory, but it would take years to collect even preliminary data. He concluded his lecture by expressing the hope that the conference would help exchange ideas, and that, through close co-operation among scientists of all nations, studies on prophylaxis and therapeutics of radiation effects would be pushed further.

The need for world-wide co-ordination of efforts in the study of the biological and especially the genetic effects of radiation was expressed over and over again at the conference. It was as if the speakers, seeing in front of them scientists from all over the world, resolved then and there to take full responsibility for the present and future well-being of the human race and told one another: "Let's get together and use our good will and ingenuity to provide protection for our progeny." The World Health Organization, an agency of the United Nations, sponsored informal discussions at the conference among biologists and physicists.

The voice of the scientists did not go unheard. On November 7, 1955, only two months and a half after the end of the conference, the Political Committee of the United Nations General Assembly voted unanimously to establish an international scientific body to co-ordinate studies and to collect and distribute data on the effects of ionizing radiation upon man and his environment. On December 3, 1955, the General Assembly adopted the resolution of the Political Committee and established a scientific committee consisting of one scientist from each of fifteen nations.

The radioactive wastes, which, it was feared, might raise the radioactive background level and thus cause genetic damage, did not escape the fierce scrutiny of the scientists at Geneva. Actually these wastes were examined from all possible sides. What were they? Where did they come from? How could they release radioactivity? How were they disposed of now, and how was it planned to dispose of them in the future?

There was no comprehensive definition of wastes given at Geneva. While nobody seemed to take into serious consideration discarded watches with luminous dials, some authors included in the list of potentially dangerous radioactive wastes the smoke emitted by hospital incinerators in which were burned clothes and bedding of patients undergoing treatment with radioisotopes, or the radon liberated during the operations of mining uranium and processing uranium ores; others limited their concern to substances from nuclear reactors and chemical reprocessing plants.

There was no possible doubt that the biggest headaches for the planners of the current and future atomic industry resulted from the high-level wastes formed in the reprocessing of spent nuclear fuel in order to recover the unburned parts. This fuel contained a very large number of fission products, of which the long-lived ones were a great nuisance. Had the wastes contained short-lived substances only, they could have been stored for a certain time, until the radioactivity decayed to a safe limit, and then dumped, like any other garbage.

Among the fission products cesium 137 and strontium 90 constituted the greatest problem, for they had half-lives of thirty-three years and about twenty years, respectively, and very high toxicity. They would have to be stored hundreds of years before their radioactivity fell below the permissible limits. Scientists and engineers envisaged larger and larger amounts of high-level wastes in the future, often dissolved in strong acids, and asked themselves, "What are we going to do with them?"

The current problems and practices of waste disposal in the United States were discussed in a paper read at a general session by Dr. Abel Wolman of the Johns Hopkins University. The wastes were being concentrated as much as possible and then stored in large underground tanks made of steel, or steel and concrete. The radioactive disintegration developed large amounts of heat, which was removed by a cooling system. The tanks were continuously monitored to detect any leak. This method was considered safe but expensive: the tanks might have to be repaired and might not last the hundreds of years the wastes would have to be stored. In England, high-level wastes were also being stored indefinitely.

Many imaginative ideas for ultimate disposal were presented at Geneva. Solutions of wastes might be dumped in Arctic desert areas, in Antarctic regions, in deserts and steppes; but transportation would be very costly. Tanks containing wastes might be dumped into the deepest parts of the oceans; the tanks could be reinforced to make sure that they did not crack on hitting the bottom. Solutions might also be dropped in the oceans in plastic containers which would remain embedded in the mud of the bottom; if strontium and cesium had been removed first, the activity would not be sufficient to destroy the resins of the bags, and leakages, if any, would be very slow. But too little was known about the movements of deep waters, their mixing and turnover, about the rate of diffusion of substances, about the biochemical behavior of the oceans. Oceanographers were studying the problem, and their reports were awaited before definite plans were made for waste disposal.

Experiments were being conducted in the United States to fix radioactive substances in certain clays. The clay that had absorbed a solution of radioactive wastes was fired in a kiln. The radioactive wastes thus fixed in the ceramics could not be appreciably leached and carried away by water; they might be safely buried under ground or stored in shielded places. Some of the fired ceramics were in the form of beads, which, it was thought, might find some use as radioactive sources. If strontium and cesium were separated from the rest of fission products and fixed in baked clay units, they might be used as radiation and heat sources.

Disposal of low-level wastes presented a lesser problem, although some quite interesting complications might arise. It may seem safe to discharge wastes into water, so long as their level does not rise above the maximum permissible level for drinking water; but it is not necessarily so, because certain aquatic living organisms can accumulate radioactive substances. It was found, for instance, that plankton and small fish in the Columbia River, in which the cooling water from the Hanford reactors was discharged, were so hungry for phosphorus that they absorbed great quantities of radiophosphorus. In a certain minnow the concentration of radiophosphorus was 150,000 times greater than in the surrounding water. So, in order to avoid radiation damage to living organisms, and contamination of fish that might be eaten by men, the level of radiophosphorus in the Columbia River was kept below that permissible for drinking water.

Similar conclusions were reached for radioactivity discharged in the air, for instance from air-cooled reactors. If reactors were in agricultural zones, as would probably be the case in England, levels of radioactivity in the air that were safe for breathing might not be safe otherwise: grazing animals might ingest radioactive substances deposited on the vegetation, in which case radio-iodine and radio-strontium would be concentrated in their milk.

No aspects of the safe disposal of radioactive wastes were without problems. Studies were being pushed vigorously in various countries, and many promising methods were envisaged. All the same, as Dr. Abel Wolman remarked in his paper, "the disposal of reactor and fuel processing wastes will be one of the major controlling factors in determining the extent of the use of power reactors; . . . the . . . total fission products on hand . . . will be prodigious. To dispose of these materials will undoubtedly challenge the ingenuity and imagination of the scientist and industrialist."

12 PLANS AND HOPES

The extent of the achievements in the field of peaceful applications of atomic energy came as a surprise to most delegates and observers. The cloak of secrecy had concealed part of the work done in some nations from the others, and even inside the same country workers in one branch of atomic science and technology had not been fully aware of progress in other branches. Scientists who had developed chemical processes for the separation of radioactive elements did not necessarily know the work of the agriculturists, and biologists were probably not acquainted with the most advanced reactor designs. The conference provided an exhaustive and yet compact survey of the field, which impressed all those trying to assess it.

Representatives of several countries candidly declared that only in Geneva had they realized how far some nations had progressed in the atomic art; others said that they had not been aware before that the "commercial" stage had been reached in the reactor field. Yet, to many of the less fortunate nations reactors were still out of reach, for they were too expensive, even the research reactors at half-price offered by the United States. To all participants in the conference, the technical papers, both those that were read and those that were not, furnished material for intense study for a long time to come. Some countries were planning to translate at least part of the papers into their national languages.

The role that the countries with the most advanced atomic programs played in the great exchange of ideas that took place at Geneva needs no illustration. But the role of the other nations may be easily underestimated, and it may be thought that in the balance of give and take the nations that had made little progress in nuclear science were entirely on the "take" side. That is not true. All peoples had their contribution to make. Although before the conference it was generally accepted as a fact that a new source of energy would soon be needed to meet the world's requirements, the details of this need and of the special forms that it took in the various countries were either not known or only vaguely understood. Thus by presenting papers on their conditions and power requirements, and, even more, by discussing their individual problems informally, many nations furnished invaluable information for the building of an atomic industry on sound and realistic foundations. The fact emerged, for instance, that the most useful type of reactor for some time to come would be a medium-sized package reactor that could be shipped or flown to remote regions where electricity was not produced or was very expensive. Reactors of this type could help develop small industries, exploit isolated mines, pump water for irrigation, drain marshes, provide air conditioning in areas that could support larger populations if only living conditions were made more pleasant.

Generalizations about the delegations cannot be carried out much further. On the other hand, limitations of space and of knowledge make it impossible to describe them in detail. A few examples will be given here, with the warning that the choice was to a large degree left to chance and is not meant to be representative.

The Italians had crossed the border into Switzerland in large numbers: ninety-seven delegates and many observers had come to the conference. Theirs was the largest delegation after those of the United States (259 members) and of the United Kingdom (135). Because the trip from Italy was easy and pleasant, many had brought their wives and children along. A few had rented summer homes for their families in the nearby mountains, and in the morning they drove to the Palais des Nations in their small cars. More stayed in town and crowded into rooms that they had planned to occupy for a few days only and then make available to others; but when the time came for them to leave, their interest had mounted so that they could not bear not to stay to the end.

The Italian delegation was headed by Professor Francesco Giordani, President of the Italian National Committee for Nuclear Research. The Italians contributed three session chairmen and one vice-chairman to the conference, and Professor Giordani was one of the chairmen. Being the owner of a thick, dark beard he was easily recognizable in the crowd of delegates, for even in that diversified assemblage of people once-popular beards were unfortunately scarce. Giordani, stocky and lively, with quick gestures always accompanying his words in truly Neapolitan fashion, became well known in Geneva.

Four Italian commercial exhibitors participated in the trade fair at the Palais des Expositions with displays of scientific instruments, and it almost seemed as if the industrialists had greater interest in the conference than the scientists.

Before the Second World War nuclear physics had flourished in Italy, and some of the basic discoveries were made there. The war had disrupted scientific research, and, even before the outbreak of hostilities in Europe, political conditions had driven several physicists out of the country. The physicists who remained had carried on, almost miraculously, through the vicissitudes of the war years. Then, with the news of the atomic bomb had come the realization of the great strides in nuclear physics made elsewhere. Italy was close to economic ruin; there were no funds available for research; and any attempt at filling the gap of knowledge appeared quite futile. So the physicists in Italy turned to the study of cosmic rays, which come free of charge from outer space. When funds for fundamental research began to be available again, it was logical that they should be used to build particle accelerators, which are factories of artificial cosmic rays. Once this decision was made, it gave a compelling reason to the physicists for sticking to high-energy and elementary-particle physics.

In 1952 the National Committee for Nuclear Research was established under Professor Giordani's chairmanship. Search for uranium that had been privately undertaken was co-ordinated and a few sparse deposits were found in the northwestern part of Italy. The National Committee assigned reactor studies to the privately owned CISE (Center of Information, Studies, and Experiments). A true incentive to these activities came only after President Eisenhower's Atoms for Peace program had gathered momentum, and the international co-operation that it made possible became a fact. In the spring of 1955 Italy entered into a bilateral agreement with the United States for co-operation and assistance in the field of atomic energy.

The willingness of the United States to enter into such agreements was announced by Ambassador Henry Cabot Lodge, Jr., in his address of November 5, 1954, before the United Nations Committee on International Cooperation on Developing the Peaceful Uses of Atomic Energy. The committee was then debating the resolution calling for the international agency and technical conference. Ambassador Lodge said: "We are prepared to start discussion with other countries for the conclusion of bilateral agreements which will make it possible for us, under our laws, to furnish technical information, technical assistance, and necessary amounts of fissionable material for the construction and operation of research reactors to be located abroad." By the time the Geneva conference took place, twenty-six countries had concluded agreements under which the United States pledged not only to give technical assistance and materials but also to contribute half the cost of the first research reactor in each country.

Italy had also bought ten tons of heavy water from the United States for its first reactor. CISE, under contract with the National Committee for Nuclear Research, was to build it.

Italy, with few natural resources, with a population of almost fifty million in an area about two-thirds that of California, had much to hope for from the advent of the atomic age. Eighty-five per cent of the power produced in Italy was hydroelectric, according to Professor Giordani's paper on Italian power requirements in 1975 and 2000. A part of the other 15 per cent was obtained by burning fuel, and the balance was produced by natural steam, through the exploitation of geysers existing in a limited region of central Italy. Hydroelectric resources were not entirely exploited, but the construction of new plants would become more and more expensive and subject to the availability of concrete and skilled manpower. Moreover, hydroelectric possibilities were poor in the South, which was the part of Italy in greatest need of power. Before 1975, Italy would be compelled to import expensive fuel unless economical nuclear power could be had.

Confronted in Geneva with the full panorama of achievements in the atomic field, the Italians, especially those from the industries, were quick to appraise the worth of the new technology. Workers at the United States technical exhibits noticed the Italian engineers in particular for their numerous and pertinent questions: they were not just looking, they were trying to learn. Representatives of United States industries at Geneva reported that the greatest number of inquiries they received about possible purchases of reactors came from the Italians. And the Italians made news when it was announced that the Fiat Company of Turin, which made cars and airplanes, had negotiated the purchase of a power reactor from Westinghouse. As it passed about by word of mouth, the announcement acquired symbolic value, for this was the first transaction for a power reactor between two private enterprises.

The near-sensation that the announcement created was soon dampened by those ever present, punctilious voices that insist on cold facts. Only Britain, Canada, and Belgium had agreements with the United States permitting construction of power reactors. Under all other bilateral agreements, only research reactors could be built as yet. On closer examination the announcement showed that the deal was tentative, subject to government approval. Meanwhile, the Geneva office of the Fiat Company received many queries about the state of the negotiations but could not answer them. They knew nothing. The president of the company had been in Geneva for a few days but had already left, and if he had bought a reactor he had not said so.

A few months after the closing of the conference, at least four Italian companies were said to be actively negotiating the purchase of power reactors from United States industries, pending an agreement on power. Fiat of Turin was still among them but had lost its symbolic primacy: private Belgian groups had bought the first commercially sold power reactor from Westinghouse, to be ready for use at the Brussels World's Fair in 1958. Belgium was in a special position as one of the main producers of uranium and had a special agreement with the United States that made the purchase possible.

After these remarks about the third largest delegation, mention of one of the smallest seems in order. A few nations were represented at the conference by one person only, and among these was Lebanon. Miss Salwa C. Nassar, a young Arab woman, was the lonely member of the Lebanese delegation, and lonely did she look as she sat among the other fourteen hundred delegates. Although all dreams are solitary, dreams about the future progress of one's country are worthless unless they can be talked over with countrymen.

Miss Nassar was chairman of the physics department of the American University in Beirut. She was well traveled and spoke English perfectly, in a serious, eager tone. She was kind to interviewers and answered questions readily. She had been notified of the conference and asked to attend it only three weeks before it started. There had been no time to prepare papers, she said regretfully. When she talked about Lebanon, she let her bright eyes wander far. Lebanon had only a million and a quarter population, and its problems were different from those of larger countries. Lebanon had entered into a bilateral agreement with the United States for assistance in the atomic field. But no practical steps had yet been taken. Shortage of trained people in nuclear science was great. There was only a handful of trained professors in physics, scattered among three institutes of higher learning. None of these conferred doctorates, which had to be obtained abroad. A few Lebanese students were specializing in the atomic field at foreign institutions. It would be good if more could enjoy this privilege, but to study abroad was very expensive for a Lebanese. Perhaps funds for research and scholarships would become available if the proposed draft for a National Scientific Research Council were accepted. The draft suggested that 1 per cent of the national budget, about half a million dollars, be devolved to the council.

They already had a cobalt-60 source of gamma rays for studies in medicine. Being a teacher of physics, Miss Nassar would welcome a research reactor, she mused—the smallest available, she added, perhaps in a return to reality. It should not be set up in Beirut, which was very crowded, but some twelve miles outside. It could become a training center for other Arab countries; she already had students from Syria and Iraq. In the long run, she could not say when, Lebanon would want atomic power; one reactor generating one hundred thousand kilowatts would be sufficient. She had already talked with delegates of other nations to find out how they would approach the problem of buying or of building a power reactor. She was very pleased with the conference; she had experienced the same surprise the Western scientists had at the friendly behavior of the Russians. She had never seen a Russian scientific paper before coming to Geneva.

The Israeli delegation numbered nine members, two of whom were diplomats permanently residing in Europe. The chairman of the delegation was Mr. Walter Eytan, Director General of the Ministry for Foreign Affairs. Israel had signed an agreement with the United States and showed remarkable interest in atomic questions.

Israel was undergoing an extraordinarily rapid development, and its electricity requirements doubled every four years, said Mr. Eytan (while the world average use of electric power was doubling every ten years). But in Israel there was no oil, no coal. A hydroelectric plant had been destroyed by the Arabs. So, from the very moment it became an independent state in 1948, Israel had looked ahead to other sources of power: atomic and solar energy. In their research the Israelis had advanced in both fields. And in 1952 the Israeli Atomic Energy Commission was established.

The Italian-born Giulio Racah, professor of theoretical physics at the Hebrew University of Jerusalem, was a member of the commission and well aware of Israel's needs. Yet, when he had first heard that a conference on the peaceful uses of atomic energy would be held in Geneva, he had decided not to go. Just another conference— probably a propaganda move. Besides, he was having a new house built for his family and wanted to supervise it. Then Bhabha, the appointed President of the conference and a theoretical physicist like Racah, had stopped in Jerusalem on one of his many trips to the West and had explained the hopes placed in the conference, the pains taken in organizing it, and the fact that only the co-operation of the best scientists of the entire world could make it successful. Racah changed his mind, and in Geneva he looked as if he were glad he had. To him, as to the many well-traveled scientists, this was a welcome opportunity of meeting again with old friends from various parts of the world, with the added zest of discussing with them what atomic energy could do for his country.

If Israel was poor in natural resources, it was rich in first-rate intellects. People to be trained in the nuclear field would be easily found, and the training could be done to a large extent at home. Israel was considering the purchase of a reactor but not an entirely prefabricated one. The Israelis would want to participate in its construction and gain experience. Some research pertinent to reactor construction was already being carried out. A method for making heavy water by distillation had been devised. The more common

electrolytic process would be too costly for a country where the shortage of electricity was as acute as in Israel.

Atomic power could be used especially for irrigation: Israel, an
arid, semitropical land, was proud of having become an agricultural
country, but agriculture could not survive without irrigation; land
reclamation already absorbed one-third of Israel's production of
power. Atomic power and agriculture were likely to be interdepend-
ent in the future. The phosphate in the large deposits that were discovered in the Negeb Desert contained small quantities of uranium;
this could be recovered at not too great a cost as a by-product of the
refining process which the phosphates had to undergo before they
could be used as fertilizer. Power was needed also to provide air
conditioning in cities at low altitude, but for this purpose solar energy seemed more promising. Israel was very rich in sunshine.

Egypt had not concluded an agreement for co-operation in peaceful atomic matters with the United States, and its current attitude
toward atomic questions was one of "wait and see." Egypt did not
want power right away and had come to the Geneva conference to
learn, said Dr. Afaf Sabri, a quiet, thin lecturer at the University of
Cairo. Dr. Ibrahim Helmi Abdel Rahman, Secretary General of the
Council of Ministers and Member Secretary of the Egyptian Atomic
Energy Commission was of the same opinion: he said with great
emphasis that, first of all, Egypt had to train people. Of course the
Egyptians wanted agreements, but before signing them they wanted
to understand what it was they were signing, what was this fissionable material that they could get, what good the quantity available
could do for Egypt, what would be the restrictions on its use.

Egypt had a five-year training program, and Dr. Rahman not
only hoped but was doing all in his power to see it completed in
three years. Dr. Rahman, broad-shouldered and wide-jawed, gave
the impression of competence and strength. With his engaging smile
he seemed to say that he felt equal to achieving the impossible.

Egypt already had too many medical doctors, and there were not
enough jobs for all. Egypt had also many engineers and some good
experimental physicists working mostly at interpreting nuclear phenomena recorded on plates which had been exposed in accelerators
of luckier countries. Under the training program, some hundred and

fifty Egyptians had been sent all over the world. Two were currently in the United States, where they were attending the first course of the reactor school at the Argonne National Laboratory, and two more had already enrolled for the second course.

Egypt was buying radioisotopes from England and using them in a new medical treatment unit. An Atomic Energy Commission had been established a few months prior to the Geneva conference to plan the course of atomic developments. Egypt did not have enough money to buy several reactors and did not want a small research reactor. What was needed was one from which to learn the technology of a truly power-producing plant: metallurgy, chemistry, separation processes, cooling systems, and heat transfer. In short, a pilot plant. Atomic power, when its time came, would do a great deal of good for Egypt. Hydroelectric resources were scarce and would soon be exhausted; already one-half of the oil used to generate electricity had to be imported. There was thorium in the sands of the delta of the Nile, and a geological survey currently under way showed a little uranium. Perhaps more would be found. Then atomic power would be used to drill much-needed wells and to lift water, which in some places was as deep below ground as six hundred feet; atomic power would help develop the country and raise the standard of living. Better conditions in Egypt would benefit not only the underprivileged there but also the inhabitants of rich countries.

As Dr. Rahman talked, his mounting enthusiasm infected his listeners, and an ecstatic glow came to light Afaf Sabri's liquid eyes.

Dr. Nazir Ahmad, Chairman of the Atomic Energy Committee of Pakistan expressed in stronger terms Dr. Rahman's thought: atomic energy would help lessen the tension in the world only if the rich countries were to share the benefits from it with the underdeveloped nations; otherwise tension would increase. Dr. Ahmad made this point several times during the conference, both officially and in the course of private interviews. "Giving knowledge is fine," he said as a comment on the amount of information gathered at the conference, the extent of which had come as a surprise to him and to his fellow members of the Pakistani delegation. "But assistance to the underdeveloped countries in using this knowledge for their own good is even more important."

Dr. Ahmad thought that the conference was a wonderful idea, for which he was grateful both to President Eisenhower and to the United Nations. It was an occasion for people of so many countries to come together and tell one another what they had been doing. In the West there had been close scientific co-operation. But among Eastern nations there had been only the looser and more generalized ties of UNESCO.

Pakistan had recently set up its Atomic Energy Committee and entered into a bilateral agreement with the United States, from which the Pakistani expected "many advantages." The grant made by the government to the committee for the current year was equivalent to about six hundred thousand dollars, "quite a sizable sum" for Pakistan. Yet, before buying a reactor, Pakistan wanted to set up a program for training atomic scientists who would intensify nuclear research and the study of possible applications of isotopes, especially in the fields of medicine and agriculture. Meanwhile, Pakistan was sending as many students as it could to the United States and England. The first group had already returned and would train others. So in a few years Pakistan might be ready to purchase a research reactor for its universities from whatever country would make the most advantageous conditions. At a later stage, plans would be made for a power reactor.

Pakistan had a population of eighty millions, increasing at the rate of a million a year. It produced very little power. Hydroelectric resources were located in two extremities of Pakistan, far from the areas where power was mostly needed; coal reserves were poor and in places where mining was difficult. Pakistan's main trouble was that it did not produce enough food, although land was not lacking. One family working on the soil produced food for 1.2 families. Atomic power could help relieve this condition in more than one way: it could drain marshes in some zones and in others lift water for irrigation. The manufacture of much-needed agricultural machinery would also require power.

At the closing session of the conference, Dr. Ahmad delivered one of several short valedictory addresses. He asked again that the more advanced countries "extend to us the hand of cooperation so that humanity as a whole might gain from the benefits of this truly remarkable development in science and so that no large areas are neglected which might become centers of tension leading to strife and struggle." He then suggested the establishment of regional centers for training in atomic science, where the trainees from groups of countries could go at little expense and where the few advanced countries would send their experts.

One delegation was peculiar in one respect at least, that it represented a state which could not possibly be looking forward to material advantages for itself from atomic energy: the Holy See. The delegation of the Holy See was composed of an Italian geophysicist, Professor Enrico Medi, and of a Genevese Dominican, Father Henri de Riedmatten. The thin, pale scientist and the plump, rosy-cheeked clergyman attended the conference assiduously and often paced the long corridors of the Palais des Nations in serious conversation. One likes to imagine that during these long perambulations the professor explained some aspects of nuclear science and the way it could be put to good use, and the Dominican commented on the spiritual value of a conference that had been made possible and was destined for success by an unprecedented spirit of good will among nations. Each of these two delegates had a chance to speak before a large audience.

At the closing plenary session, Professor Medi remarked that the Spiritual Power that his delegation represented never ceased to exhort that the resources of which the world was endowed by its Creator should be made available to everybody. In praising the conference and emphasizing its success, he noted that it had not embraced all sides of the problem; that social and economic factors should be examined to insure the distribution of the newly acquired wealth to the less fortunate. Such a step in the utilization of atomic energy for peaceful purposes had been hoped for and encouraged by the Holy Father sixteen months earlier, when in an Easter message he had said: "We urge all men of science and good will to persevere with boldness and confidence in the theoretical and experimental study of fissionable preparations and materials, in order to obtain a considerable output of easily accessible energy to be applied where it is necessary to relieve the pressure of need and poverty."

Father Henri de Riedmatten had his chance to speak on the Sunday that marked the mid-course of the conference. On that day, at eight-thirty in the evening, a Pontifical Mass was celebrated in the Basilica of Our Lady, in connection with the international conference. The Bishop of Lausanne, Geneva, and Fribourg officiated, and Father de Riedmatten preached the sermon for the occasion. The Catholic Federation of Geneva invited the conference delegates to the Mass.

To the many Catholic delegates, the Mass provided a welcome spiritual interlude. The immensely high vaults of the old basilica invited the soul to expand. The voice of the organ, low at first and then stronger, spreading through the Gothic arches resounded in those vaults, became fuller and richer. A herald came in from a side door, garbed in gold and blue, holding a halberd that pointed straight upward. He led the way for the procession. This came in slowly, the Cross in front, then the officiants in their golden vestments, the clerics in white, the Bishop in all the magnificence of his liturgical garments, with the pastoral in his right hand. In front of the altar the elaborate ritual was performed with lofty solemnity. In the pews, which bore the names of their customary occupants, the delegates prayed, genuflected, and rose in reverence, then made ready to hear the sermon. From the pulpit Father de Riedmatten, in the white robe and black cloak of the Dominican, addressed the delegates.

He hailed the conference as an auspicious sign of peace. He begged the scientists not to forget the demands of mankind but to see that the new energy be applied where it was necessary, as the Holy Father had requested. He warned them not to fall into the easy illusion that the golden era was to come on the morrow. Above all, he warned them of the spiritual dangers that men incurred in the modern, "industrial" era. "Distances between continents or countries are no longer a problem, but the distance between souls has never been so great," he said. His full voice became more sonorous as with outstretched hands he pointed his chubby fingers toward the delegates. Scientists, he went on, were not the creators of the wonders they discovered, and at every step of their work they witnessed the presence of God. They should not allow that atomic energy be used for the destruction of the material and spiritual assets of mankind. Happiness could be found only in the glorification of God for the new blessing that he had bestowed on mankind.

13 *AND SO THE END*

Several references to the evening lectures have been made in the preceding pages, and only a few remarks remain. Ten lectures were delivered in five evenings evenly distributed throughout the twelve working days of the conference. The distribution of the lectures themselves was not so even: one lecture on the first night, two on the second, four on the third, and then, symmetrically, two on the fourth and one on the fifth.

The reader knows already that one night (the second) the lectures were devoted to accelerators and that the speakers were Lawrence of the University of California and Veksler of the U.S.S.R.; he also knows that Hollaender of Oak Ridge and Kursanov of the Soviet Union talked on biological subjects (on the fourth night); and that on the last night Sir John Cockcroft, with his usual clarity and brilliance of exposition, gave a concise picture of the technical topics discussed at the conference.

The evening of the first lecture held a surprise. The speaker was Professor Niels Bohr of Denmark. After the President of the conference, Bhabha, introduced him, all the people in the audience got to their feet and applauded, and they did the same at the end of the lecture, in a tribute that they did not give the other speakers. But this was not surprising, because Bohr was the best known and possibly the most cherished of all living scientists. When the prolonged applause subsided, Bohr began to speak, and through their earphones the English-language listeners heard perfectly pronounced and clear words. Now, Bohr's indistinct low whisper, like some sort of introspective mumbling, and the vaguely Danish intonation of his English were as famous as the man himself.

Startled at first, the listeners beamed. The secretariat of the conference had provided an English "translation" of Bohr's English, and the translator was so skilful that many in the audience took some time before realizing that the words did not come out of Bohr's mouth. So for the first time and with no strain the English-speaking scientists grasped each of Bohr's words. Later some delegates claimed that they had listened to Bohr's voice directly with one ear and to the "translation" with the other, and they had noticed no time lapse between the two.

Bohr's address, "Physical Science and Man's Position," was a philosophical interpretation of modern atomic physics and quantum mechanics, in which Bohr saw a lesson that "may even contribute to a broadening of the relationships between human societies with different cultural traditions." In the development of modern atomic physics, Bohr said, physicists were often confronted with phenomena that apparently contradicted the laws of classical physics. This contradiction led them to revise the fundamental concepts and to construct a wider conceptual framework in which contrasting experiences could be harmonized.

The first step in this direction was taken by Albert Einstein, who revised the ideas of "space" and "time" in his theory of relativity and "gave our world picture a unity surpassing previous expectations." At the same time, the study of atomic phenomena showed that their observation could not be kept separate from the conditions under which they were observed; for instance, an atomic particle, much too small to be seen directly, could be revealed through its action on a photographic plate. The plate, however, slowed the particle and thus affected its energy; only if taken together did the particle and the photographic plate give a description of the atomic phenomenon under study. This is what Bohr called "complementarity." The principle of complementarity was found to be widely valid in quantum mechanics.

To the uninitiated persons in the audience, Bohr's philosophy seemed not the easiest possible, despite the beautiful enunciation. Especially hard to follow were references to the "mathematical formalism of quantum mechanics which contains the classical physical theories as a limiting case"; and to the "non-commutative algorithm involving Planck's constant." To Bohr, however, the most difficult ideas seemed to come easily and gently, helped by a rhythmic swinging back and forth of his whole body, which he balanced on his outstretched arms, while his hands grasped the edges of the table. He wore a light-gray suit, and at the distance that divided him from the audience he appeared all silvery gray, like the gray desk lamp that shone on him. All in the audience, both those who understood what he meant and those who did not, listened intently, almost holding their breath, for all were in awe of the man, of the place, and of the occasion.

When Bohr transferred his principle of complementarity from wave mechanics to biology, his meaning became clearer. On living organisms, he said, no exhaustive chemical and physical experiments could be performed which did not menace life itself, and a compromise had always to be made between the thoroughness of the experiment and the preservation of life. Complementarity became even more easy to grasp when Bohr applied it to psychology and pointed out that the description of behavior unavoidably involved introspection, that the study of psychological phenomena could never be entirely dissociated from "the background indicated by the word 'ourselves.' "

These approaches, the principle of complementarity and the "striving for harmonizing apparently contrasting experiences by their incorporation in a wider conceptual framework," could be applied to human societies with different cultural backgrounds and to the promotion of their mutual understanding. "Just the difficulty of appreciating the traditions of other nations on the basis of one's own national tradition suggests that the relationship between cultures may rather be regarded as complementary."

Bohr concluded his lecture by remarking that science played a great role as a unifying element of human culture, through co-operation in scientific research. He expressed the hope that the conference would become a landmark in this respect. "We trust," he said, "that the opportunity of intercourse and acquaintance offered at this great occasion will essentially promote the common striving for the elevation of culture in all its aspects."

On the evening of August 15, when four lectures were delivered, the Assembly Hall was used for the two which seemed to hold the greatest popular appeal: "Radioactive Tracers and Their Applications," by Professor George de Hevesy of Sweden, and "Radiocarbon Dating," by Commissioner Libby of the United States. At the same time, in a smaller hall, Dr. Hans Bethe of Cornell University and Professor Louis Leprince-Ringuet of France spoke on elementary particles, describing some of the many kinds of "mesons" discovered in recent years.

A general comment on elementary particles may be made, in the mood of Bohr's philosophy. Modern physics has fostered the building of a wide, unifying conceptual framework but has given the physicists a large variety of bricks with which to build. It was once believed that the elementary particles, of which everything in nature was made, were the "atoms," the "indivisible" of the Greeks. Later the atom was believed to be made of two different kinds of particles, the electrons and the protons. In recent years many more "elementary particles" have been found: neutrons, positrons, mesons, hyperons, etc. While the world picture as seen from Bohr's viewpoint became more and more unified, examined on the basis of types of particles of which all matter is made, this same picture showed increasing disunity.

Some of the elementary particles were theoretically postulated before their existence was experimentally ascertained. One example is striking. Two elementary particles of mass 1 were known, one having a positive electric charge, the proton, the other having no charge at all, the neutron. Reasons of symmetry, comparison with other sets of particles and other theoretical considerations indicated that another particle of mass 1, having a negative charge, ought to exist. The particle, that had not been found in nature, was given the name "antiproton." In his Geneva evening lecture Bethe disclosed that a group of physicists in Berkeley were looking for the antiproton in very high energy experiments with the bevatron. He predicted that the group would be successful. It was. The antiproton was discovered, and its discovery was announced by the Berkeley group only a couple of months after Bethe's prediction.

The same evening in which Bethe lectured in the Assembly Hall, Professor de Hevesy recalled the early work with radioactive tracers, which started before the discovery of artificial radioactivity, when all the radioactive substances available for experimental investigations came from a single uranium mine owned by the imperial Austrian government: the mine at Joachimsthal in Bohemia. He was working at the time with Rutherford at the Cavendish Laboratory in London and experimenting with the solubility of lead and radium salts. Later, artificial radioactivity, the cyclotron, and finally the nuclear pile "opened up a fairyland."

Professor de Hevesy showed several slides, as most of the other speakers did. The requests for slides, made by delegates in various languages, various foreign accents of the same language, and various degrees of clarity, occasionally upset the operator of the projector. The conference staff must have worried about possible confusion and delay, for in his report Mr. Urquhart remarked on this point and stated that few of the requests for slides "were up to the standard of old world courtesy set by Professor de Hevesy, who, for each slide, would make a low bow to the operator and say in stentorian tones: 'La prochaine plaque, s'il vous plait, Monsieur!' " His changing from English, in which he was addressing the audience, to French for the sake of the operator was one sign of that courtesy.

Of the ten evening lecturers, Dr. Libby was the only one who, besides slides, showed real objects. He carefully unwrapped an odd assortment of old-looking things in front of his puzzled audience. There was a shoe "woven of grass rope by an ancient artisan, some 9,000 years ago in . . . the State of Oregon." It was found with its mate as one of three hundred pairs, in a cave buried by the eruption of an ancient volcano. There was a piece of frayed rope from Peru, two thousand years old, and there were ten-thousand-year-old droppings of an extinct giant ground sloth, found in Nevada. The ages of these specimens and of others had been determined by measuring the amount of radiocarbon (carbon 14) that they contained.

Radiocarbon dating had its origin in the sewers of Baltimore. In 1947, in the methane of those sewers, Libby and a group of coworkers found natural radiocarbon. Brooding over the significance of their discovery, the researchers were led to a series of assays and investigations, and eventually to the use of the radiocarbon content of mummies, old bones, fossils, and numberless other things for determining their age.

Radiocarbon, Libby said, is formed some six or seven miles, on the average, above our heads, in the top part of the earth's atmosphere, by the action of the neutrons in the cosmic rays upon the nitrogen of the air. Radiocarbon is a very long-lived substance, its half-life being about fifty-five hundred years. Eventually it reverts to nitrogen. If the intensity of the cosmic rays has remained constant for a time that is long with respect to the radiocarbon life, an equilibrium is reached: as much radiocarbon is created as decays into nitrogen, and the total amount of radiocarbon on our earth is constant.

Radiocarbon, once formed high up in the atmosphere, combines with the oxygen in the air and forms carbon dioxide. Atmospheric carbon dioxide is fixed by plants in the process of photosynthesis. Thus all plant life contains radiocarbon. So do animals, because they live on plants. In addition, inorganic carbonates and bicarbonates dissolved in the sea, which are in interchange equilibrium with atmospheric carbon dioxide, contain radiocarbon. During its very long life, radiocarbon in the air and in the sea is thoroughly mixed and evenly distributed.

That this is so was ascertained by Dr. Libby and his collaborators, who performed measurements of radioactivity on samples taken from all parts of the world. In the course of these assays Libby—though he did not mention the fact in his lecture—had occasion to order a shipment of penguin meat from some polar land.

The radiocarbon dating method is based on the fact that all living organisms contain the same proportion of radioactive carbon and that, when they cease to live, the assimilation of radiocarbon ceases. "The radiocarbon present in the body at the time of death then proceeds to disappear at its immutable rate of one half every 5568 years. Therefore, we expect that a 5600-year old mummy or piece of tree or cloth or flesh will show one-half the specific radioactivity observed in living organic matter at the present day and that one 11,200 years old would show one quarter, etc. The radiocarbon content of dead matter accordingly reveals the age of the specimen, the age being taken as time elapsed since death rather than . . . since birth."

So Libby and his group, and other groups as well, set themselves to measure the ages of ancient things that had once been alive. To test the validity of the method, they used samples of known age, like the Dead Sea Scrolls and scraps of wood from the coffins of Egyptian mummies. They found their calculations in good agreement with the known facts. They looked for traces of the oldest men. "We were afraid," Libby said, "that we should find man older than the last ice age, and had agreed that this would constitute sufficiently conclusive evidence to discredit the whole method." Dr. Libby concluded his lecture by saying that the evidence seemed to answer favorably the question of the validity of the radiocarbon dating method, but more time was needed for a final answer.

The evening lectures were in general better attended than the conference officials had hoped, a fact that proved the delegates' indefatigable eagerness to absorb knowledge. Only one evening did the great Assembly Hall look sparsely populated, and there was a reason: on that evening a free boat ride was offered, unofficially, by the Westinghouse Company. The boat is said to have anchored in mid-lake for a while, and to have returned the delegates to Geneva only in the small hours of the night.

Delegates and their wives seemed on the whole quite willing to seize the numerous opportunities for light amusement offered in connection with the conference, and they crowded the "socials." This attitude might be decried by the more austere critics, as it was by Dr. Gunnar Randers of Norway at the closing session. He then expressed the view that scientific co-operation could flourish even in the absence of receptions and refreshments—which is very true. On the other hand, perhaps one of the main purposes of the conference was to re-establish friendly personal relations between scientists of East and West. The socials, with their moderate offering of alcohol, of cheerful noise and small talk, helped promote these relations.

Most of the official receptions were held in the late hour of the afternoon, between the closing of the scientific sessions and the late European dinner time. Most were in hotel halls, where the guests, always in larger numbers than expected, shook hands with hosts in receiving lines and raided refreshment tables if they could manage to reach them, cutting their way through thick crowds. They started interesting conversations, raising their voices above the unceasing din, and soon found themselves without listeners, theirs having been captured and taken away by other delegates.

Memorable was the French party on a lake steamer, which gave a chance to several hundred people to cruise Lake Leman for three hours. Despite the mischievous rain that kept the guests off the open decks, all had an exceedingly good time. In the following days there was much talk of champagne and jellied chicken, of brandy and dances. (Oh! these earthy delegates and wives who gave so much thought to good food and drinks!)

The Swiss and Geneva authorities, as if they had not done enough by being hosts to the conference, invited all participants to a garden party in the Parc des Eaux Vives. The nine hundred representatives of the information mediums were invited, and so were the observers, the delegations' staffs, the conference secretariat. The park, one of those beautiful European gardens with graveled paths around perfectly trimmed lawns, shadowed by ancient trees, extended over sloping ground with a villa on its highest part. Tents had been set up around the villa, against the possibility of rain, and everywhere, both in the villa and under the tents, were tables with drinks and dainty sandwiches. It was a pleasure to walk in the park when dusk approached and made the old trees look almost black; and it was surprising, during these perambulations on vast grounds peopled by so many persons, to run often into old friends.

The United States delegation was outstandingly hospitable. On August 9 Chairman Strauss, on behalf of the Atomic Energy Commission, gave a luncheon to the principal United Nations officers of the conference and presented to them the introductory volume of the eight-volume set of "Selected Reference Material." On the afternoon of the same day the United States representatives to the conference offered a very well attended reception at the Hôtel des Bergues to representatives of other delegations.

Two days earlier there had been a reception for all members of the United States delegation and its staff, for officials of the United States Consulate, for the Swiss who had worked at the United States technical exhibits. Mrs. Lewis L. Strauss thought that there had been close to seven hundred and fifty people, and she ought to have known, for she was in the receiving line and shook hands with everyone. Not all guests were able to stay long at that party: the United States technical exhibits had opened that same day, August 7, and the men on duty took a little time off in turns to attend the reception. They arrived from the reactor building with exciting news of the first large visiting crowds and of the public's unmistakable interest.

Among the persons made happy by this news was a distinguished-looking, tall and slender man in a dark-blue suit, the Swiss Monsieur Junot. On behalf of the contractor, Conrad Zschokke, he had supervised the construction of the reactor building and the setting-up of the technical exhibit in the Palais des Nations. Once the work and the worries were over he had perhaps felt a bit let down; now, quietly and a little shyly, he listened to the reports about the public reaction, which gave him a measure of his own contribution to the success of the conference.

At these receptions, at formal and informal luncheons and dinners, Mrs. Strauss admirably filled the role of hostess of the United States delegation and seemed to be enjoying her guests. Her role as hostess kept Alice Strauss busy all through the conference and up to the very last moment. After the closing session, the Strausses gave a farewell party for a few friends in their suite at the Hôtel du Rhône, and in the friendly atmosphere the guests lingered on. This was the only time when Mrs. Strauss appeared slightly uneasy. In the end she admitted that she and her husband were to leave Geneva in an hour and that their suitcases were not packed! So the guests finally left, wishing their hosts the happiest return trip, with no misadventures, not even such a small one as had bothered Mrs. Strauss on her way to Geneva: upon setting foot on the ground at Gander airport, the strap of her shoe had ripped off, and she had made ready to hop, on her husband's arm, across the field. But the Admiral, always chivalrous with ladies, especially with his wife, had bent down, pulled out a stapler from his brief case, and stapled the strap to the shoe.

The yardstick by which success is measured often varies with the person who performs the measurement. It may be of interest to see how Mr. Charter Heslep of the information office of the United States delegation evaluated the conference. *His* yardstick was clearly one that would not occur to a scientist to use. He said:

"The Associated Press never filed less than 5,000 words a day. . . . Reuters and United Press never got a 'hold down' order from London or New York. The eight radio and television studios that the United Nations has . . . at Geneva were taxed to capacity. The estimate just from this traffic is not less than 900,000 words recorded. There were a dozen radio correspondents from different countries such as Turkey, Egypt, India, Austria, etc., who recorded 30 minutes every day. The USIA [United States Information Agency] filed more than 150,000 words and the posts all around the world were calling for more. The Peaceful Atom made page one of the *New York Times* for 10 out of the 12 days of actual sessions. . . ."

In all, the nine hundred reporters said as many words about the conference in writing or in broadcasts and films as would fill some forty good-sized novels. These estimated four million words did not include technical papers or official records of the conference sessions. The coverage of the conference by the information mediums was not only extensive but also remarkably good: science was made understandable to the layman and often exciting, although sensationalism was in general avoided.

This incredible result was not accidental; much careful planning had made it possible. Yet it surprised even those who had prepared it, for, as Heslep remarked, sex, conflict, and money, the three traditional elements of good news stories, were entirely lacking at the conference.

That information on atomic energy ought to be disseminated as widely and as objectively as possible had been early recognized at the United Nations. How this would be achieved had not been clear at once. During the late spring and early summer more and more correspondents had been notifying the United Nations of their intention to cover the conference and had asked for a press card and a bed to sleep in. This second request, although quite sensible, was not easily dealt with. The Geneva housing authorities were already facing great difficulties, with the steady and rapid increase in the numbers of all classes of participants in the conference.

The difficulty of "briefing" an uncertain number of correspondents—estimated at five hundred some six weeks before the conference and actually nine hundred—may not be as evident as the difficulty of housing them. It was nonetheless acutely felt by Professor Whitman. The reporters themselves had repeatedly expressed doubts on their ability to understand the technical subjects and to interpret the language of the scientists for the public. If chaotic and misleading reports were to be avoided, somebody would have to explain the mechanics and the substance of the conference to the information people. This somebody, or rather these, for no one single person could undertake the whole job, needed special qualities of scientific competence, ability to explain, and patience. Professor Whitman well knew who filled these qualifications: his scientific secretaries. Still he was hesitant. With his habitual objectivity he viewed his secretaries at work, weighed the task at hand and that to come, and found their shoulders pretty heavily loaded.

Eventually an ingenious system was worked out. If the journalists did not feel up to the difficulties of the technical sessions, they did not need to attend them. They could gather at noon and at five in the hall that was fully wired and provided with earphones for simultaneous translations and set aside for press conferences and wait there for a small procession to come in: The three chairmen, the three vice-chairmen and three scientific secretaries on duty at the three concurrent sessions just ended, and the principal speakers. The procession found seats behind a long speakers' table and the "briefing" started in the usual four languages, under the competent lead of two moderators, Mr. Clifford Mosbacher and Mr. Matthew Gordon of the United Nations conference information staff. First a scientific secretary summarized the content of the session in concise and plain terms, then the reporters could question the scientists at their will.

Under fire of these questions, the "brains" or "longhairs," as the newsmen liked to call the scientists, did remarkably well. "Unexpected . . . was the surprising skill shown by the scientists themselves . . . in making these briefings useful and newsworthy. And in answering frankly most of the questions asked," commented Charter Heslep.

These briefing sessions, often lasting well over an hour, a good part of the lunch recess or of the evening, *did* place an extra burden on the scientific secretaries; but this burden, being shared with other scientists and engineers, was easier to bear. After the briefing ended and within an amazingly short time—approximately one hour—tall stacks of press releases in four languages about the technical sessions were set out in orderly display on a table in front of the pressroom. And they went like the proverbial hot cakes.

Not only the United Nations but also the major countries had come to Geneva well prepared to keep the press objectively informed. Outstanding was the information office of the United States delegation, which had a two-way function of receiving and giving out news, under the direction of Mr. John P. McKnight. The press office was set up in two spacious rooms that opened into the lobby of the Hôtel du Rhône.

The visitor who chanced there at any time during the conference was faced with the mild confusion peculiar to newsrooms and consisting of desks and tables, of books and papers, of telephones and typewriters, of men and women, all scattered seemingly at random. John McKnight, tall and thin, with brown curly hair, often paced the floor, as absorbed and unseeing as if he were a scientist. In white shoes, he walked softly, stopping to ponder in front of one of the two teletype machines that steadily poured out news dispatches from around the world. A couple of magazines mentioning the conference on their covers bulged out of the pockets of his light corded jacket.

Mr. Morse Salisbury, the long-time director of the Atomic Energy Commission Information Service, sat or stood, invariably blue-suited, behind his desk and rapidly scanned printed sheets, marking the margins in pencil with precise gestures. He had not much leisure: his was the task of keeping the United States delegation informed of the goings-on; of helping to prepare statements and releases issued by the OIC; of arranging for special briefings of correspondents with a nonconformist taste in the selection of the topics they wanted to cover. At another desk Charter Heslep was always busily talking on a telephone. Only now and then he managed to exchange a few words with some delegate or newsman patiently sitting by him. Girls in colored sweaters clipped newspapers, consulted a Webster dictionary while trying to relieve the fatigue from overwork by sipping fruit juices, or sat at typewriters that hurried busily with noisy patter.

Mimeographed press releases of the OIC or digests of scientific papers were stacked everywhere on large central tables and on smaller ones along the walls, and between them moved young men sorting out papers for the stacks; stuffed drawers stuck out of filing cabinets; the teletypes received on the two machines hung on a metal frame, and from a picture on a wall President Eisenhower watched the scene.

John McKnight had been "borrowed" from the office of the United States Information Agency in Rome, whence in early June he had returned to the States to help with the press side of the conference. Later that month he had attended a press conference with Chairman Strauss and Dr. Weil at the Overseas Press Club in New York. After the other two men had spoken and been questioned, he gave some practical advice to the correspondents, such as, "Geneva is high priced . . . take nylons and wash them yourselves," and then stated, "I don't know a thing about atomic energy . . . but we will do our best to be helpful and get you to people who do know. Admiral Strauss has assured us that the total brains of the American delegation will be at your disposal to elucidate these esoteric mysteries."

Facts surpassed expectations, and the "brains" proved truly willing to help the press in Geneva. Charter Heslep, who was in charge of arranging the interviews—for this reason he was always talking on the telephone—later said that to his knowledge there was only one instance in which it was not possible to deliver a "body." Occasionally if the "body" requested was not available, the one delivered was a "substitute body," a scientist in the same field.

One tends to speculate whether the delegates would have evinced the same degree of co-operativeness had they been aware of being considered brains or bodies rather than full-fledged living beings. Be that as it may, they were helpful even before the conference started. The information office of the OIC had undertaken in the spring to prepare plain-language summaries of technical papers. Finding the task very difficult, the information people asked the authors of the papers to write the press digests themselves. Most of them did, in a clear and intelligible way. Very few sent digests as hard to understand as the papers, or declared that their work could not be put in popular form.

By August 8, 206 out of 210 press digests were ready for distribution, to the great satisfaction of Charter Heslep, who had supervised the project.

Nothing has yet been said about one of the major activities of the conference secretariat: the publication of the proceedings of the conference. So far as it is known, the first views about publishing the technical papers were exchanged between Walter Whitman and Robert Charpie in New York, around the middle of April.

Both men were in favor of an early, detailed consideration of the task of preparing these proceedings. A large amount of material was to be presented at Geneva for the first time, and scientists and technologists all over the world would be eagerly waiting for this material to be made available to them. The proceedings ought to be published as soon as possible after the conference. They would constitute the first comprehensive, exhaustive, and co-ordinated source on all phases of atomic science. It was clear that they would not all fit in one volume but would have to be divided in several volumes. It was also clear that, since the United Nations would take care of their publication, they ought to be published in the four official languages. It all sounded very sensible, but the task appeared of great magnitude, even at that time, when it was thought that some five hundred papers might be submitted to the conference, and no one dreamt that their number would exceed one thousand.

While talking, Professor Whitman studied and appraised the broad shoulders of the younger man. When Charpie left Whitman's office, he had received the title of editor-in-chief and had agreed to assume the responsibility of organizing the publication.

It was only in early July, after the work of selecting the papers for oral presentation and of shaping the conference program was well under way, that Charpie "began to spend more and more . . . time worrying how to organize the proceedings." It was clear that the Russian publication would have to be done in Russia, as all translations of papers in or from Russia were already being done, through the courtesy of the U.S.S.R. government. It was also clear that the English publication could be pursued at a much more rapid pace than the French or the Spanish because most of the oral presentations at Geneva, and a large portion of all the papers, were in the English language. Accordingly, the first editing endeavors were concentrated toward an early English publication.

There were going to be sixteen volumes, organized along the lines of the agenda. However, all the material on a single subject was to be incorporated into a single volume. Thus the reactor discussions at the general sessions would appear in the volume on power reactors. This was going to be Volume III of the proceedings, but, having perhaps the greatest popular appeal, it was to be published first. The tentative publication date for this volume was set at December 1.

When all other scientific secretaries left for Geneva, and Charpie remained behind, preparing to become a father for the second time, he took all papers for this volume home to Oak Ridge. It had been decided that the verbatim records would be published along with the papers. They were of course not available yet, since the sessions had not started. The responsibility for editing the verbatim records was undertaken by the other scientific secretaries, most of whom stayed on in Geneva for a week after the closing of the conference to attend to this task. Volume III, off the press, was presented to the Secretary-General, Mr. Hammarskjöld, in an informal ceremony on December 6.

Meanwhile the task of editing the material for the other volumes was divided among the scientific secretaries, a few of whom returned to New York after the closing of the conference. The help of other persons was engaged, and Mr. Clifford Mosbacher, the same man who had been moderator at the press-briefing sessions in Geneva, gave his able assistance as managing editor. Never before had the United Nations undertaken such a vast publishing job in so short a time. Into the sixteen volumes went eight million words, and numerous charts, diagrams, illustrations, and slides. The scientific secretaries worked hard. They had the wholehearted co-operation of all in the United Nations printing section, which had been enlarged to meet the demands of the huge task.

The preparation of the French and Spanish versions of the proceedings was organized in Geneva, under Mr. Palthey, and was advancing at a good pace.

The conference, like all good things, had to come to an end. But not before hopes were expressed that it would be repeated. On August 16, at a luncheon before the American Club of Geneva, Chairman Strauss announced that he had just received a message from President Eisenhower in which the President stated his hope "that a second conference will be convened at a later date to continue this great beginning of international cooperation." The President believed that the interval between conferences ought to be gauged to allow for a significant accumulation of new scientific knowledge and that the period might be two or three years.

Nikolai A. Bulganin, Chairman of the Council of Ministers of the Soviet Union, sent a message to the conference, the last paragraph of which read: "The Soviet Government congratulates all taking part in the Conference on the success achieved and expresses the hope that international cooperation in the field of the peaceful utilization of atomic energy, which has been so successfully inaugurated at this Conference, will be continued through the regular convening of similar meetings of scientists from all countries."

The message was read by Homi Bhabha during the farewell speech that he delivered in his capacity of President of the conference. It was Saturday, the twentieth of August, and the representatives and delegates had convened in the Assembly Hall in general session for the last time.

At this session Dr. A. N. Lavrishchev of the Soviet Union set forth in detail his country's program of international co-operation in the peaceful applications of atomic energy. He described the help that the Soviet Union was already giving to the neighboring countries, the experimental piles and the particle accelerators being designed for them, the training of their scientists in the Soviet Union, the distribution of radioisotopes. He also stated that this co-operation would be extended to other nations.

Then Dr. Willard Libby read a parallel paper describing the international program of the United States. It had been a busy day for Bill Libby: in the morning he had presented the United States Technical Library to the United Nations. At noon he had participated in the ceremony of transferring the pool reactor to the Swiss. Now the strain of the present day, and of those past, told on his face, as it told on the faces of the people who had put much time, much energy, and all their good will into the work for the conference. Libby was pale and weary as he rose to speak. He recalled President Eisenhower's address of December 8, 1953, and the position that the United States had taken toward the creation of an international atomic energy agency. He said that the United States had taken steps in advance of the formation of this agency and that during the previous six months it "has been disclosing to the world a good deal of its fund of information gained through the American people's immense outlay of time and treasure and energies."

He then enumerated the measures taken by the United States to assist other countries in the development of their own atomic programs: the shipments of isotopes; the courses in handling radioisotopes at the Oak Ridge Institute of Nuclear Studies; the postdoctoral training at Atomic Energy Commission hospitals; the technical libraries assembled for presentation to those desiring them; the School of Nuclear Science and Engineering at the Argonne National

Laboratory; the bilateral agreements for exchanges of information on the peaceful applications of atomic energy and for the construction of research reactors. In this last regard Libby emphasized the hope and expectation that these agreements would eventually be extended to allow construction of power reactors.

Sir John Cockcroft then made an informal statement of the British international program. Representatives of various countries followed with brief remarks, some of which were mentioned in chapter 12. Professor Pierre Auger of the United Nations Educational, Scientific and Cultural Organization (UNESCO) presented the problems and the methods of training men in the new atomic art. Bhabha concluded the session with his presidential farewell, in which he briefly stated the main results of the conference, thanked "those very few countries, most advanced in this field, which have so wholeheartedly and generously placed before this conference the knowledge . . . gained during the last decade through such strenuous efforts and at such great cost," and read Bulganin's message mentioned above.

And this was the very end of the conference.

From the Assembly Hall the delegates went out into the Salle des Pas Perdus and lingered for the last time with friends new and old. They talked once more of their gratification about the conference in tones betraying the almost unreal atmosphere of elation and euphoria that they had gradually created in Geneva, through their anxious yearnings for co-operation and friendliness, through their zeal and their faith in the possibility of achieving what they had set themselves to achieve.

Slowly, the Salle des Pas Perdus became empty again, and appeared monumental in its marmoreal splendor. Soon among those marbles there was to be placed a tablet commemorating the conference, which would say, in French:

"In this building, on August 8, 1955, nuclear scientists representing seventy-three nations came together to share and exchange their knowledge for the benefit of mankind at the First International Conference on the Peaceful Uses of Atomic Energy, convened by unanimous resolution of the General Assembly of the United Nations."

ACKNOWLEDGMENTS

It is impossible to list here all the people who have helped me in the preparation of this book. Most of the persons mentioned in it have taken time either to talk to me and explain their work or to furnish data, read parts of the manuscript, and give me the benefit of their criticism. But others, both at the Atomic Energy Commission and elsewhere, have been just as kind and helpful, and were not mentioned either because they were not directly connected with the conference or, if they were, because of lack of space. To all of them I am deeply grateful.

I wish to make special acknowledgments to Mrs. Vance L. Sailor and to Dr. Herbert L. Anderson. In Geneva, where so much went on at the same time, Mrs. Sailor was a most valuable, acute observer and exhaustive reporter; thus she relieved me from the impossible duty of being in several places at once. Dr. Anderson painstakingly read the entire manuscript and, through discussions and suggestions, considerably clarified my understanding of scientific subjects.

INDEX

Accelerators: bevatron, 120, 121, 204; CERN, 122; Cockcroft and Walton, 12; cosmotron, 120, 121, 122; cyclotron, 50–51, 74, 120; French, 169; Italian, 191; Russian, 120–22, 216; synchrotron, 120; synchro-cyclotron, 120, 122

Adrian, Edgar D., 13

Advisory Committee to conference: established, 17; first meeting, 18–20; second meeting, 13, 37–39; third meeting, 70

Agenda, 11–14, 18, 19, 20, 37

Ahmad, Nazir, 197–98

Alpha particles, 12, 43, 50, 51–52

Amaldi, E., 73

Ambulance, Swedish radiological, 152, 177

"American Attorney," 148

"American Jurist," 134–35

Anderson, Clinton P., 51–52, 53–54, 182–83

Antiproton, 204

Antwerp dock strike, 135

Appert, Nicholas, 36

Arco, lighting of, 162

Argonne National Laboratory, 134, 140; Borax tests, 159–63; carbon-14 biosynthesis, 147–48; reactor training school, 16, 197, 216; reactors, 141–42, 156, 158, 163

Associated Press, 209

Atomic bomb, 41, 85, 87, 88, 89

Atomic Energy Act: of 1946, 27; of 1954, 10, 12, 28

Atomic Energy Commission (U.S.): Advisory Committee on Reactor Safety, 155; Committee of Senior Reviewers, 28, 63; Division of Classification, 28, 29; established, 8; fusion research, 88–89; General Advisory Committee, 7, 9, 20; Reactor Development Division, 22; training program, 16, 197, 216–17

Atomic fuel, 16, 46; *see also* Fissionable material; Fuel elements; Plutonium; Reactor fuel; Uranium

Atomic Industrial Forum, 148

Atomic pile; *see* Reactors

Atoms for Peace Awards, 107

Atoms for Peace program, 4, 7, 8, 9, 15, 76, 109, 191; presented at U.N., 5–7

Auger, Pierre, 74, 217

Australia, 16, 149, 154

Baehni, Charles, 131

Barros, Jayme de, 17

Baruch, Bernard M., v

Becquerel, Henri, 49, 173

Belgian Embassy, Washington, 135

Belgium, 16, 135, 193

Bermuda conference, 5, 9

Bethe, Hans A., 74, 85, 203, 204

Bhabha, Homi J., 17–19, 74, 86–88; on Advisory Committee, 18; closing address, 216, 217; President of conference, 20; presidential address, 76–78, 84–85, 89

Big Four Conference, Geneva, 3, 60, 66, 105

Bilateral agreements, 109, 191–92, 193, 194, 195, 198, 217

Binks, W., 182

Biosynthesis, of labeled compounds, 53, 147–48

Blokhintsev, D. V., 117, 156–57

Bohr, Niels, 73, 82, 146, 201–3

Borax tests, 159–63

Boron, in brain-tumor therapy, 147

Boveri, Walter, 109

Brandy Rock (Va.), 8, 15

Brazil, 17

Brecker, Richard, 29–30, 134–35

Breeding (in reactors), 47–48

Breycha Vauthier, A. C., 151

Bronk, Detlev W., 61

Brookhaven National Laboratory, 11–12; brain-tumor therapy, 146–47; gamma